OCCUPATION UNDER SIEGE

OCCUPATION UNDER SIEGE

Resolving Mental Health Crises in Police Work

By

JOHN M. VIOLANTI, PH.D.

New York State Police, Retired

CHARLES C THOMAS · PUBLISHER · LTD.
Springfield · Illinois · U.S.A.

Published and Distributed Throughout the World by

CHARLES C THOMAS • PUBLISHER, LTD.
2600 South First Street
Springfield, Illinois 62704

© 2021 by CHARLES C THOMAS • PUBLISHER, LTD.

ISBN 978-0-398-09376-1 (paper)
ISBN 978-0-398-09377-8 (ebook)

Library of Congress Catalog Card Number: 2021029741 (print)
2021029742 (ebook)

With THOMAS BOOKS *careful attention is given to all details of manufacturing
and design. It is the Publisher's desire to present books that are satisfactory as to their
physical qualities and artistic possibilities and appropriate for their particular use.*
THOMAS BOOKS *will be true to those laws of quality that assure a good name
and good will.*

Printed in the United States of America
MM-C-1

Library of Congress Cataloging-in-Publication Data

Names: Violanti, John M., author.
Title: Occupation under siege : resolving mental health crises in police
   work/ by John M. Violanti, PH.D.
Description: Springfield, Illinois : Charles C Thomas, Publisher, Ltd.,
   [2021] | "New York State Police, Retired"--Title page. | Includes
   bibliographical references and index.
Identifiers: LCCN 2021029741 (print) | LCCN 2021029742 (ebook) | ISBN
   9780398093761 (paperback) | ISBN 9780398093778 (ebook)
Subjects: LCSH: Police--Job stress--United States. | Police--Health and
   hygiene--United States. | Police--Mental health services--United States.
   | Police psychology--United States.
Classification: LCC HV7936.J63 V56 2021 (print) | LCC HV7936,J63 (ebook)
   | DDC 363.201/9--dc23
LC record available at https://lccn.loc.gov/2021029741
LC ebook record available at https://lccn.loc.gov/2021029742

This book is dedicated to Dr. Douglas Paton—
Scholar, friend, and distinguished researcher.

Sincere thanks and gratitude to all of those
police officers who daily "drive and walk
the beat" and keep us safe from harm.

PREFACE

These are challenging times for police in the United States and throughout the world. The men and women who work in this profession are not only challenged by social activism, divisive politics, and a pandemic but also on a psychological and physical personal level. We all are aware of the danger of being a police officer, but beneath that lies a hidden danger: mental distress. A successful police career therefore involves not only surviving the danger but also psychological survival.

I wrote this book because I wanted to bring the research community and police practitioners to the realization that there is a crisis in health among the police. My past years as a police officer and researcher has brought me to this conclusion. In this writing, I have included a mixed approach which includes research and some practical suggestions from practitioners on how best to deal with the police health crisis.

The book is based on research associated with police mental health together with the subsequent effects on officer's performance, physical health, and lifestyle. The first chapter outlines the current challenges face by police, increased civil unrest, negative public reactions, and a biological siege brought about by the COVID-19 pandemic. These events have caused personnel shortages, long work hours, and psychological and physical assaults upon the police.

In Chapter 2, discussion turns to the present mental health status of police officers. Posttraumatic Stress (PTSD) and depression appear to be prevalent in police. Police officers are repeatedly exposed to traumatic situations including motor vehicle accidents, armed conflicts, and witnessing violent death across their working lives. An estimated 7%–19% of police officers qualify for a diagnosis of PTSD, and approximately 34% experience a number of PTSD symptoms. Depression and PTSD are often found together in officers. Several studies on police have found the prevalence of depression to be approximately 12% which is nearly twice as high as the general population. Both depression and PTSD promote poor health through a complex interaction between biological and psychological mechanisms. Police officers with PTSD or depression are at an increased risk for negative health issues such as cardiovascular disease and gastrointestinal disorders, comorbid psychological conditions as well as suicide. Officers with severe PTSD symptoms are approximately three times more likely to have the metabolic syndrome—a collection of components which increase the risk for heart disease. Faced with responding to fatal accidents, crime, child abuse, homicide, suicide, and rape, police officers become hopeless because of the futility of preventing such events. Lack of organizational support is also associated with significantly increasing levels of hopelessness. Police officers have a high risk of burnout. Officers report that they experience significantly high levels of cynicism, exhaustion, and lowered professional efficacy, three facets of burnout. Police burnout has been associated with organizational and operational stress including lack of support from the community or the lack of promotion. Consequences of burnout can include substance abuse, decreased quality of service, and impaired mental and physical health.

The effects on mental well-being among police officers is not limited to service time. There may be factors which occurred in the officer's life prior to entering service and after the officer leaves. There are two dynamics outside of police service discussed in this chapter: officers (1) prior personal childhood abuse; and (2) retirement from police work. Research is limited on the association of prior child abuse and the mental health of police officers. Once in police work, officers are exposed to multiple trauma and stress. They see many of the evils of society, which include the types of child abuse they themselves suffered. This can trigger trauma responses. Exposure to child abuse on the job only further thwarts their sense of justice, leading to frustration and hopelessness. A recent communication with police mental health professionals suggested that 25% of all police clients had a history of childhood abuse or neglect. After service, retirement is a significant life event for police officers. The loss of police identity is difficult for officers. Leaving police work does not always reduce mental strife; often there are vestiges of trauma and loss. Although some officers eagerly await retirement, it signals the end of relationships and routine. The police subculture is a closed society where officers maintain a sense of strong cohesion and dependence upon one another for survival. It is not easy for police officers to leave this interpersonal web of protection. Under such conditions, one would expect that retired officers may likely be prone to mental issues. Lastly discussed in this chapter are reasons why officers are hesitant to ask for help with mental difficulties. A number of factors affect an officer's willingness to come forward including law enforcement identity, mental health stigma, and fear of reprisal.

Research in the area of police suicide highlights Chapter 3. The police have an increased risk for suicide. In today's societal and politically conflicted environment, the police are caught between the requirements of the job and the ability to fulfill these requirements. Negative public scrutiny, exposure to trauma, violence and mass murders, riots, unappreciated risks—sometimes risking their lives—coupled with any personal problems in living all add up to the inability to cope. A sense of isolation results among police coupled with frustration, pent up aggression, and eventual depression fueled by exposure to trauma, death, abused kids, murder and human misery. Officers die by suicide to escape the unendurable psychological pain brought about by work exposure.

Chapter 4 discusses the effects of police stress and trauma on physical health. The stress and trauma that police face can eventually wear down the body's defense against disease. With present day intensification of stress on police, we may see increasing health problems in the future. The police suffer from increased rates of cardiovascular disease, cancer and other illnesses. Mental health problems such as depression, post-traumatic stress disorder (PTSD), and other anxiety disorders have been found to be associated with physical illness. Chronic stress can disrupt the cardiovascular system as well as other bodily functions leading to wear and tear on the body and to psychological, metabolic, inflammatory, and cardiovascular disease. The stress of shift work also has a significant health impact on health.

Resilience is discussed in Chapter 5 and its role in ameliorating stress. Resilience is simply defined as bouncing back from adversity. There are, however, many dimensions of resiliency to consider. It has long been believed that exposure to trauma inevitably leads to pathologies such as PTSD and depression. Recent research in the area of positive psychology has opened the realization that these pathologies do not occur in all people. In police work, where high stress events and exposure to potentially traumatic events is common, recovery is essential. This chapter provides an overview of factors related to resilience and examines some of the mechanisms that underpin resilience in police work. Additionally suggestions are made which may help police organizations foster resiliency in officers. It is important that the protective characteristic of resilience against stress be explained and employed in the profession of policing.

Chapter 6 asks the question, "Where do we go from here?" The chapter discusses current legislation which will help police deal with the problem of psychological, physical health, and suicide. Interventions discussed include the need for wellness programs, reducing stress through the police organization, peers support development, the use of mindfulness as a stress reduction strategy, PTSD mitigation, and reducing the fatigue health effects of shift work. Lastly, a summary of results are listed from the Buffalo Cardio-Metabolic Occupational Police Stress (BCOPS), a 16-year longitudinal study on police health and psychological well-being led by this author.

I sincerely hope that this book will help researchers and those dedicated officers who go out every day and "drive and walk the beat." It is those officers who bear the brunt of policing. There is hope.

J.M.V.

CONTENTS

FIGURES

OCCUPATION UNDER SIEGE

HIGH STRESS TIMES: POLICE UNDER SUBSTANTIAL PRESSURE

The years 2020 and 2021 were unprecedented for U.S. police. Troubling incidents stemming from humankind and nature together brought turmoil for the police. Protests and riots had to do with certain inflammatory police arrest incidents and political unrest. Much of the civil unrest and protests in 2020 appeared to start from an incident involving the arrest of a black man in Minneapolis, Minnesota. On May 25, 2020, George Floyd, a 46-year-old black man, was arrested by police for using a counterfeit bill. During the arrest, Mr. Floyd died while under restraint. The officer involved was charged with third-degree murder, second-degree manslaughter, and second-degree murder. Floyd's death triggered worldwide protests against police brutality, police racism, and lack of police accountability. As a result, the police faced an unprecedented backlash. Protests often coupled with violence erupted through the world, causing monumental destruction of property, injury and even death. The Floyd death initiated a strong negative sentiment against the police, leading to explanation of other deaths by police involving black citizens, at times going back many years.

DISRUPTIVE SOCIETAL CORRELATES OF POLICE MENTAL HEALTH: CIVIL UNREST, RIOTS, AND PANDEMICS

Civil unrest, protests and riots are nothing new and in many cases mental health pathology has been noted after such events. The effects on police of civil unrest and social disruption have been studied over many years. Harvey-Lintz and Tidwell (1997) examined the psychological effects of the 1992 Los Angeles civil disturbance on the levels of PTSD symptomatology among police officers during the riots. A substantial number of police officers assigned to riot areas experienced PTSD symptomatology, and were dissatisfied the way the department provided support.

Ni et al. (2020) conducted a systematic review of mental health outcomes associated with Hong Kong, China riots. Prior to the riots, the reputation of the Hong Kong Police was stellar but was severely damaged by violent response to the riots by police (Hong Kong protests, https://en.wikipedia.org/wiki/2014). Ni et al. (2020) found that depressive symptoms were the most frequently assessed outcome of all studies, followed by PTSD and anxiety symptoms. Depression among police was 1.5% before the riots and increased to 8.5% six months afterwards Ni et al. (2020). Other outcomes included psychiatric admissions, psychological stress and suicide. Ni et al. (2020) also found that proximity to violence was one of the most important predictors for depression and PTSD. Direct victims of looting, arson and physical injury demonstrated the highest levels of PTSD (Ni et al., 2020). Social media increased stress with users holding different ideological views (Ni et al., 2020).

Garbino et al. (2012) studied the effects of protests on Italian "VI Reporto Mobile" officers, a specialized group used to handle high risk public safety events. Similar to the Hong Kong police, the violent riots that occurred during the G8 Summit in 2001 damaged the reputation of Italian police forces. The support afforded to the police was minimal, even worsening the psychological well-being of officers. Galovski et al. (2016) examined the exposure to violence that occurred in Ferguson, Missouri in 2014 and the shared mental health effects on police and community. They looked at proximity to violence—connectedness, direct exposure, fear from exposure, media exposure, reactions to media, and life interruption—as correlates of PTSD symptoms, depression, and anger. Results indicated that trauma and stress were shared among both the police and members of the community. Proximity to events during the protest was a strong predictor of negative mental health outcomes.

Figure 1.1
Police Perceptions of Stress Factors Associated with Civil Unrest

Negative Public Perceptions

Distorted or negative media accounts of police

*Undue criticism of police, experiencing negative
attitudes toward police officers; public apathy toward police*

*Dealing with people who abuse the police (examples:
riots, confrontations with aggressive crowds;*

*physical attack on one's person; possibility of injury on the
job; personal insults from citizens*

*Unreasonable expectations during riots or demonstrations
from those outside the department*

Political pressure from within the department    ***STRESS***

Political pressure from outside the department

Outside interference with police work during the unrest

Departmental handling of complaints against officers not fair

Doing things I don't agree with in bad situations

Low morale

Difficulty staying objective (not expressing my emotions)

Not receiving recognition for a job well done

As a result of the stress associated with recent civil unrest many officers decided to leave police work. An article by the Christian Broadcasting News (2020) stated the following:

> Police are retiring early in unprecedented numbers. The push to
> defund police departments, massive budget cuts and calls for police
> reform, have left officers demoralized and demonized so they are
> walking off the job. In Seattle, a video goes viral after a police offi-
> cer tells a Black Lives Matter protestor that he's quitting. "Don't worry

to social isolation, fear of infection, unemployment, and vast exposure to death all add this dilemma. Marcelo Leiva-Bianchi et al. (2018), in a meta-analysis of psychological effects of disasters, concluded that people exposed to disasters such as COVID-19 show higher negative psychological impact. The threatening event decreases coping ability and reduces resources for help. The most exposed groups have fewer resources to cope with the disaster and will have more probabilities of responding negatively to it. The loss of mobility such as lengthy quarantine, employment, and social relationships all increase the risk of psychological impact (Marcelo Leiva-Bianchi et al., 2018). Studies of natural disaster survivors found that the one-year prevalence of PTSD has been reported to be as low as 5% and as high as 60%. Several months to years after a natural disaster, during which time persons experience a reduced quality of life and decreased productivity (Breslau, Kessler, Chilcoat, Schultz et al., 1998). COVID-19 has been associated with symptoms of anxiety, depression, trauma, and suicidal ideation and higher rates of drug and alcohol abuse (Czeisler et al., 2020). A survey conducted by the Centers for Disease Control and Prevention found that of 5,470 responds, 40.9% reported an adverse mental or behavioral health conditions during COVID-19 (Czeisler et al., 2020). Unsurprisingly, higher rates of anxiety and depression have also been reported in health care workers (Vindegaard & Benros, 2020).

First responder health workers in a Beijing hospital reported high depression symptoms three years after the Severe Acute Respiratory Syndrome (SARS) pandemic. Depressive symptoms were associated with pre-SARS traumatic experiences, quarantining, and high perceived risk as well as high PTSD symptoms (Liu et al., 2012). In another study, the SARS virus was associated with burnout, psychological distress, and increased use of alcohol and tobacco (Maunder et al., 2012). Among hospital staff working in Toronto during SARS, two-thirds reported feeling concern for their own and their family's health (Nickell et al., 2004). These studies showed the negative psychological effects of a large-scale epidemic on workers on the front line. Similar findings have been found in the persons with COVID-19 who have been working during COVID-19 in health care. Wang et al. (2020) found that 54% of their sample rated the psychological impact of the COVID pandemic as moderate to severe. Oiu (2020) found that 35% of the sample reported psychological distress. Social isolation, economic problems, lock downs and fear associated with COVID-19 was associated with mental anguish. Holingue et al. (2020) suggested that mental distress is increasing because of COVID-19.

COVID-19: Police Mental Health Risks

As of this writing, the Federation of Police (FOP, 2020) reported that 282 officers have died through the U.S. from COVID-19. In terms of impact, the COVID-19 pandemic may be considered a major disaster and there are certainly tragic repercussions in society at large. How persons in authoritative positions such as police address this pandemic is a matter of concern because it not only affects the people they serve but also themselves. Police officers need to remain both mentally and physiologically healthy and be ready to perform at their peak during such crises. The number of deaths and illness that follows COVID-19 have produced undue strain on first responders such as law enforcement. Issues currently confronting police departments include reduced staff, insufficient safety measures and equipment and poor organizational support (Alexander & Ekici, 2020; Lum et al., 2020). These studies indicate that police departments are under a great deal of stress and at greater risk because of COVID-19 (Alexander & Ekici, 2020; Bates, 2020). Stress affects multiple systems in the body and can have several mental and physical health consequences (Hubbard & Workman, 1998; McEwen & Lasley, 2003).

COVID-19 is not the first epidemic that the police have had to deal with. In 1981, HIV/AIDS (human immunodeficiency virus) was discovered and still is considered a pandemic by the World Health Organization (WHO). As of 2018, approximately 37.9 million people are infected with HIV globally (UN Aids Data, 2021). Similar to COVID-19, the police encountered the risk of HIV infection by contact with the public in their everyday work. Flavin (1998), in her investigation of police and HIV exposure, found that police were at potential risk because of certain activities they perform in their work. Exposure to blood, body fluids and tissue, administering CPR, possible needle sticks, being spit on, and body contact during a scuffle while making an arrest were some possible factors for transmission of HIV. All of these may similarly expose officers to COVID-19.

Figure 1.2
COVID-19 Risk Factors and Potential Psychological Effects on Police

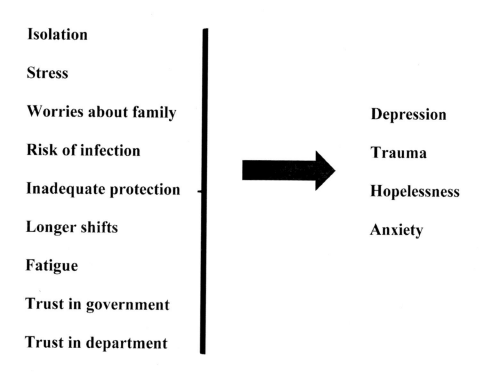

COVID-19 Risk factors　　　　　　　　**Psychological Effects**

Isolation

Stress

Worries about family

Risk of infection　　　　　　　　Depression

Inadequate protection　　　　　　Trauma

Longer shifts　　　　　　　　　　Hopelessness

Fatigue　　　　　　　　　　　　　Anxiety

Trust in government

Trust in department

Police officers are frequently exposed to a quickly changing landscape, which can result in very high levels of mental and physical stress (Maria et al., 2018; Marmar et al., 2006). The response to COVID-19 is no different. Issues currently confronting police departments include reduced staff, insufficient safety measures and equipment, and poor organizational support (Alexander & Ekici, 2020; Police 1, 2020). A recent survey indicated that 35% of police departments had suspended their police academies, 12% had increased overtime hours, and approximately 30% had to furlough staff due to COVID 19 (Lum et al., 2020b). Although exact figures are not known, in April, 17% of the New York Police Department were out sick and five officers had died (Bates, 2020). Since then, rates of COVID-19 have not only increased in the general population but also in police populations. Currently, it has been estimated that thousands have test-ed positive (Bates, 2020; Johnson, 2020). Those that have been done indicate that police are under a great deal of stress due to COVID (Alexander & Ekici, 2020; Bates, 2020).

Stogner et al. (2020) reported that law enforcement officers are experiencing increased occupational stressors due to changes brought about by COVID-19. Officers are expected to coordinate local shut-downs, encourage social distancing, and enforce stay-at-home laws compounded by understaffing and underfunding. Several municipali-ties have recently defunded departments even more after high profile negative incidents involving the police.

- First, they were expected to implement new policies to ensure social distancing while stay-at-home directives were challenged on political, economic, and legal grounds.
- Second, they were required to adapt existing practices had to be adapted to limit exposure and ensure enough officers remained healthy to maintain public safety.
- Third, agencies clearly suffered from shortages in PPE (Personal Protection Equipment).
- Fourth, the COVID-19 pandemic itself was a traumatic event, pre-senting consistent risk of bodily harm and requiring officers to be increasingly hypervigilant of their own environment. The daily exposure to stress, safety protocols, and social distancing policies may have limited their capacity to engage in positive coping strate-gies.
- The threat of COVID-19 and the challenges of social distancing policies presents a particular problem for small rural law enforce-ment agencies.

(Stogner et al., 2020.)

Future Preparations

The police were caught unprepared for the COVID pandemic. It is essential that they now increase training and prepare for a possible second and third wave of the virus (Stogner et al., 2020). Experiencing trauma or highly stressful events can overload an individuals' adaptive response, challenge their understanding of the world and result in mental and physical health issues (Hubbard & Workman, 1998; McEwen & Lasley, 2003). This may be particularly true of police officers who have been charged with protecting the public, maintaining civil order, and dealing with their own personal losses. Fenkel et al. (2020) commented that the police can manage effective performance during the pandemic by intervention at the organizational level:

- Stockpile Personal Protection Equipment, including masks, gloves, gowns, eyewear, and hand sanitizer, to ensure an immediate and sufficient supply at all times.
- Keep the number of staff on duty at a minimum to avoid infection
- Limit the interaction with the public. Focusing on critical incidents or major crimes
- Suspend protocols that put people in custody or handling non-violent and non-emergency calls via telephone
- Keep communication and information channels open.
- Leaders need to train and regularly update officers on COVID-19.
- Strengthening individual coping resources through training would help officers to deal with the stress they face.

The police faced similar risks with the AIDS epidemic. Flavin (1998) in her paper on police and HIV exposure pointed to a listing of educational tools that should be applied in order to deal with HIV. This list may be applied to COVID-19 as well:

- Provide accurate information about how the virus is and is not transmitted
- Defuse unwarranted fears and anxieties about contact with infected persons, including coworkers
- Educate officers on universal precautions, as well as the potential for infection during arrest, first aid, search, and crime scene processing activities
- Tie the content explicitly to departmental policies and procedures
- Involve staff in the development of training programs and materials
- Education should take place prior to a job-related exposure incident
- Offer on an ongoing basis
- Evaluate component to assess the content, quality, and effectiveness of the training program
- Provide to all officers, regardless of their assignment. (Flavin, 1998)

There are other resources that can protect officers from the negative effects of stress, including organizational support, resilience, and active coping. Organizations and supervisors that foster trust through understanding, support, and encouragement can reduce feelings of stress, enhance feelings of competence, and increase feelings of cohesion (Violanti, 2014). Support has also been shown to be an important component of resilience (Bonanno et al., 2007; de Terte & Stephens, 2014; Turner & Marino, 1994). Resilience is the ability to overcome negative experiences (Bonanno, 2004; Southwick et al., 2014). Resilient workers are less likely to experience symptoms of PTSD following a traumatic event (de Terte & Stephens, 2014). Individuals with high resilience are also more likely to display optimism, use coping skills, and cultivate positive emotions such as humor to overcome difficult experiences (Fredrickson et al., 2003). Similarly, active coping includes planning, acceptance or seeking support and is associated with higher well-being and lower psychological distress, depression and anxiety (Kaur et al., 2013; Maran et al., 2015). In contrast, avoidant coping behaviors such as self-blame, disengagement, or denial is associated with higher depression and perceived work stress (Gershon et al., 2009; Kaur et al., 2013; Maran et al., 2015). Rather than engage in denial or avoidance, coping skills can be used to mitigate the effects of stress.

The optimal performance of the police, especially during a pandemic is dependent on tangible resources such as the availability of personal protective equipment, but also their mental and physical wellness. Police are potentially challenged with multiple stressors such as social stigmatization, lack of protective equipment, and witnessing human suffering and death (Lum et al., 2020; Vena et al., 2013). Under these circumstances, the overall psychological and physical well-being is likely affected (Kim et al., 2011; Violanti, 2014). If the COVID-19 outbreak persists or there is a resurgence, it may induce long-term mental health issues such as symptoms of PTSD, depression, or anxiety. Psychological well-being, in turn is associated with worsened job attitudes, higher turnover, decreased job performance, and health issues (Violanti, 2014). Mental and physical wellbeing are essential for police to perform efficiently and successfully carry out their mandate to serve and protect.

Although there is an increasing recognition of the psychological challenges faced by the police during the COVID-19 outbreak, we still do not understand how mental and physical well-being will be affected over time in such a dynamic environment, where the virus spread-induced risks are evolving every day. Efficiently performing police are key to successful societal functioning of law enforcement and taking care officer's overall well-being is of importance. The government and police organizations need to understand the risk for long-term severe mental health problems among police while working in a disaster framed environment for prolonged time, and make informed decisions about preparedness strategies that may help in minimizing such risks during any other dynamic extreme event (Syed S. et al., 2020).

Intervention studies need to be designed to reduce the health consequences of occupational stressors among law enforcement officers and potentially other emergency responders occurring due to disaster situations. This can lead to improvements in physical and psychological well-being with a potential for reduction in the burden of disease among officers very necessary service to society. Such information will better inform us in our work to develop specific interventions for stress and illnesses in policing and help to prepare for similar events such as disasters and epidemics.

In the next chapter, discussion will center on the present mental health status of police. If societal conditions persist as they are, the expectation is that mental health among police will only worsen over time deepening this crisis.

REFERENCES

Amsalem D., Dixon L. B., & Neria, Y. (2021). The coronavirus disease 2019(COVID-19) outbreak and mental health: current risks and recommended actions. *JAMA Psychiatry, 78,* 9–10. PMID:32579160 https://doi.org/10.1001/jamapsychiatry.2020.1730

Alexander, D. C., & Ekici, N. (2020). Survey: COVID-19's impact on LE operations. In Police 1 (Ed.). Lexipol.

Bates, J. (2020). Police departments, sheriffs' offices across the U.S. grapple with COVID-19's impact on public safety—and their own. Time. *Time.* USA, LLC, online.

Bonanno, G.A. (2004). Loss, trauma, and human resilience: Have we underestimated the human capacity to thrive after extremely aversive events? *American Psychologist, 59,* 20–28.

Bonanno, G. A., Galea, S., Bucciarelli, A., & Vlahov, D. (2007). What predicts psychological resilience after disaster? The role of demographics, resources, and life stress. *Journal of Consulting Clinical Psychology, 75,* 671–682.

Breslau, N., Kessler, R. C., Chilcoat, H. D., Schultz, L. R., Davis, G. C., & Andreski, P. (1998). Trauma and posttraumatic stress disorder in the community: The 1996 Detroit Area Survey of Trauma. *Archives of General Psychiatry, 55*(7), 626–632. https://doi.org/10.1001/archpsyc.55.7.626

Christian Broadcasting News (CBN). (2020). https://www1.cbn.com/...s/2020 /september/demoralized-and-demonized-police-departments-face-workforce -crisis-as-officers-leave-in-droves [10/9/2020 2:42:37 PM]

Czeisler M. É., Lane, R. I., Petrosky, E. et al. (2020). Mental Health, Substance Use, and Suicidal Ideation During the COVID-19 Pandemic—United States, June 24–30, 2020. MMWR Morbidity and Mortality *Weekly Report, 69,* 1049–1057. doi: http://dx.doi.org/10.15585/mmwr.mm6932a1external icon

de Terte, I., & Stephens, C. (2014). Psychological resilience of workers in high-risk occupations. *Stress and Health: Journal of the International Society for the Investigation of Stress, 30,* 353–355.

Flavin, J. (1998). Police and HIV/AIDS: The risk, the reality, the response. *American Journal of Criminal Justice, 23,* 33–58. https://doi.org/10.1007/BF02887283

Fredrickson, B. L., Tugade, M. M., Waugh, C. E., & Larkin, G. R. (2003). What good are positive emotions in crises? A prospective study of resilience and emotions following the terrorist attacks on the United States on September 11th, 2001. *Journal of Personality and Social Psychology, 84,* 365–376.

Frenkel, M. O., Giessing, L., Egger-Lampl, S., Hutter, V., Oudejans, R. R. D., Kleygrewe, L., . . . Jaspaert, E. (2021). The impact of the COVID-19 pandemic on European police officers: Stress, demands, and coping resources. *Journal of Criminal Justice, 72,* 1–14. [101756]. https://doi.org/10.1016/j.jcrimjus.2020 .101756

Garbarino, S., Carlo, C., Magnavita, N., Piattino, S., & Giovanni, C. (2012). Personality profiles of special force police officers. *Journal of Police and Criminal Psychology. 27,* 99–110. https://doi.org/10.1007/s11896-011-9099-6

Galovski, T. E., Peterson, Z. D., Beagley, M. C., Strasshofer, D. R., Held, P., & Fletcher, T. D. (2016). Exposure to violence during Ferguson protests: Mental health effects for law enforcement and community members. *Journal of Traumatic Stress, 29*(4), 283–292.

Gershon, R. R., Barocas, B., Canton, A. N., Li, X., & Vlahov, D. (2009). Mental, physical, and behavioral outcomes associated with perceived work stress in police officers. *Criminal Justice and Behavior, 36,* 275–289.

Guo, Q., Zheng, Y., Shi, J., Wang, J., Li, G., Li, C., . . . Fromson, J. A. (2020). Immediate psychological distress in quarantined patients with COVID-19 and its association with peripheral inflammation: A mixed-method study. *Brain Behavior Immunity, 88,* 17–27.

Harvey-Lintz, T., & Tidwell, R. (1997). Effects of the 1992 Los Angeles civil unrest: Post traumatic stress disorder symptomatology among law enforcement officers. *The Social Science Journal, 34*(2), 171–183. doi: 10.1016/S0362-3319(97)90049-5

Holingue, C., Kalb, L. G., Riehm, K. E., Bennett, D., Kapteyn, A., Veldhuis, C. B., . . . Johnson, R. M. (2020). Mental distress in the United States at the beginning of the COVID-19 pandemic. *American Journal of Public Health, 110*(11), 1628–1634. https://doi.org/10.2105 /AJPH.2020.305857

Hong Kong protests. https://en.wikipedia.org/wiki/2014_Hong_Kong_protests

Hubbard, J. R., & Workman, E. A. (Eds.). (1998). *Handbook of stress medicine: An organ system approach.* CRC Press: Boca Raton, FL.

Kaur, R., Chodagiri, V. K., & Reddi, N. K. (2013). A psychological study of stress, personality and coping in police personnel. *Indian Journal of Psychology Medicine, 35,* 141–147.

Leiva-Bianchi, M., Cornejo, F., Fresno, A., Rojas, C., & Serrano, C. (2018). Effectiveness of cognitive-behavioural therapy for post-disaster distress in post-traumatic stress symptoms after Chilean earthquake and tsunami. *Gaceta sanitaria, 32*(3), 291–296. https://doi.org/10.1016/j.gaceta.2017.07.018

Liu, X., Kakade, M., Fuller, C.J., Fan, B., Fang, Y., Kong, J., . . . Guan, Z. (2012). Depression after exposure to stressful events: Lessons learned from the severe acute respiratory syndrome epidemic. *Comprehensive Psychiatry, 53,* 15–23.

Lum, C., Maupin, C., & Stoltz, M. (2020a). The impact of COVID-19 on law enforcement agencies (wave 1). A joint report of the International Association of Chiefs of Police and the Center for Evidence-Based Crime Policy, George Mason University.

Lum, C., Maupin, C., & Stoltz, M. (2020b). *The impact of COVID-19 on law enforcement agencies (wave 2).* A joint report of the International Association of Chiefs of Police and the Center for Evidence-Based Crime Policy, George Mason University.

Maran, D.A., Varettoc, A., Zedda, M., & Ieraci, V. (2015). Occupational stress, anxiety and coping strategies in police officers. *Occupational Medicine, 65,* 466–473.

Marcos, C. (2021). Second police officer dies by suicide after Capitol attack. https://thehill.com/homenews/house/536189-second-police-officer-dies-by-suicide-after-capitol-attack. Accessed 2-23-21.

Maunder, R. G., Halpern, J., Schwartz, B., & Gurevich, M. (2012). Symptoms and responses to critical incidents in paramedics who have experienced childhood abuse and neglect. *Emergency Medicine Journal, 9,* 222–227.

McEwen, B. S., & Lasley, E. N. (2003). *The end of stress as we know it.* Washington, D.C.: Joseph Henry Press.

Neria, Y. (2020, September). *COVID-19 and mental health: Implications for police force.* Police Resiliency Symposium, New York City, NY. Virtual presentation.

Ni, M. Y., Kim, Y., McDowell, I., Wong, S., Qui, H., Wong, I. O. L., . . . Galea, S. (2020). Mental health during and after protests, riots and revolutions: A systematic review. *Australian & New Zealand Journal of Psychiatry, 54*(3), 232–243. doi: 10.1177/00048

Nickell, L. A., Crighton, E. J., Tracy, C. S., Al-Enazy, H., Bolaji, Y., Hanjrah, S., . . . Hussain, A. (2004). Psychosocial effects of SARS on hospital staff: survey of a large tertiary care institution. *Canadian Medical Association Journal, 70,* 793–798.

Pappa, S., Ntella, V., Giannakas, T., Giannakoulis, V. G., Papoutsi, E., & Katsaounou, P. (2020). Prevalence of depression, anxiety, and insomnia among healthcare workers during the COVID-19 pandemic: A systematic review and meta-analysis. *Brain Behavior Immunity, 88,* 901–907.

Police COVID-19 deaths. https://www.nysfederationofpolice.com/

Qiu, J., Shen, B., Zhao, M., Wang, Z., Xie, B., & Xu, Y. (2020). A nationwide survey of psychological distress among Chinese people in the COVID-19 epidemic: Implications and policy recommendations. *General Psychiatry, 33*(2), e100213.

Southwick, S. M., Bonanno, G. A., Masten, A. S., Panter-Brick, C., & Yehuda, R. (2014). Resilience definitions, theory, and challenges: Interdisciplinary perspectives. *European Journal of Psychotraumatology, 5,* 14.

Stogner, J., Miller, B. L., & McLean, K. (2020). Police stress, mental health, and resiliency during the COVID-19 Pandemic. *American Journal of Criminal Justice, 45,* 718–730. https://doi.org/10.1007 /s12103-020-09548-y

Syed, S., Ashwick, R., Schlosser, M., Jones, R., Rowe, S., & Billings, J. (2020). Global prevalence and risk factors for mental health problems in police personnel: A systematic review and meta-analysis. *Occupational and Environmental Medicine, 7,* 737–747.

Turner, R. J., & Marino, F., 1994. Social support and social structure: a descriptive epidemiology. *Journal of Health and Social Behavior, 35,* 193–212

UN Aids Data, UNAIDS.org. 2019. Retrieved 22 Feb. 2021.

Vahratian, A., Blumberg, S. J., Terlizzi, E. P., & Schiller, J. S. (2021). Symptoms of anxiety or depressive disorder and use of mental health care among adults during the COVID-19 pandemic—United States, August 2020–February 2021. *Morbidity and Mortality Weekly Report, 70,* 490–494. doi: http://dx.doi.org /10.15585/mmwr.mm7013e2

Vena, J. E., Charles, L. E., Gu, J. K., Burchfiel, C. M., Andrew, M. E., Fekedulegn, D., & Violanti, J. M. (2013). Mortality of a police cohort. *The Journal of Law Enforcement Leadership and Ethics, 1,* 7–30.

Vindegaard, N., & Benros, M. E. (2020). COVID-19 pandemic and mental health consequences: Systematic review of the current evidence. *Brain, Behavior, and Immunity, 89,* 531–542. https://doi.org/10.1016/j.bbi.2020.05.048

Violanti, J. M. (2014). *Dying for the job: Police work, exposure and health.* Springfield, IL: Charles C Thomas, Publisher, Ltd.

Wang, C., Pan, R., Wan, X., Tan, Y., Xu, L., Ho, C. S., & Ho, R. C. (2020). Immediate psychological responses and associated factors during the initial stage of the 2019 coronavirus disease (COVID-19) epidemic among the general population in China. *International Journal of Environmental Research and Public Health, 17*(5), 1729. https://doi.org/10.3390/ijerph17051729

Chapter 2

THE MENTAL HEALTH STATUS OF POLICE OFFICERS

It's not stress that kills us, it is our reaction to it.

—Hans Selye

INTRODUCTION

This chapter will focus on psychological factors related to mental health in police work: (1) post-traumatic stress disorder (PTSD); (2) depression; (3) hopelessness; (4) burnout; and (5) events in the life course of officers (child abuse and retirement).

The conditions and exposure associated with police work are a fertile area for adverse mental health outcomes. Syed et al. (2020) conducted a meta-analysis estimating the prevalence and risk factors for mental health problems among police personnel worldwide. The overall prevalence was 14.6% for depression, 14.2% for post-traumatic stress disorder (PTSD), 9.6% for a generalized anxiety disorder, 8.5% for suicidal ideation, 5.0% for alcohol dependence, and 25.7% for hazardous drinking. The strongest risk factor for depression and suicidal ideation was higher occupational stress, and the strongest risk factors for PTSD were higher occupational stress and avoidant coping strategies. Syed et al. (2020) also found that police mental issues were associated with poor social support, occupational stress and maladaptive coping strategies. Fox et al. (2012) reported that 24% of their police sample reported PTSD, 9% depression, and 19% alcohol abuse. Only 46.7% had ever sought mental health services. A survey study by Jetelina et al. (2020) on 446 officers found that 12% reported a lifetime mental health diagnosis, and 26% had positive screening results for current mental illness symptoms. The findings suggest that depression, anxiety, and suicidal ideation or self-harm, which typically take longer to manifest, also should be systematically addressed in police work (Jetelina et al., 2020).

POST-TRAUMATIC STRESS DISORDER (PTSD)

Symptoms of PTSD include re-experiencing trauma, avoidance, negative cognitions and mood, arousal often manifested by aggressiveness, sleep problems, and recklessness or self-destructive behavior (DSM-5, American Psychiatric Association, 2013). Police officers are repeatedly exposed to traumatic situations including motor vehicle accidents, armed conflicts, and witnessing violent death across their working lives (Marmar et al., 2006). An estimated 7%–19% of police officers qualify for a diagnosis of PTSD, and approximately 34% experience a number of PTSD symptoms but do not meet a full PTSD diagnosis (Carlier, Lamberts, & Gersons, 1997; Robinson, Sigman, & Wilson, 1997). Following a traumatic incident, a number of different factors have been found to affect whether an individual will develop PTSD. These factors include a prior history of trauma, coping styles, irregular work hours, rotating shifts, and lack of social support both inside and outside work (Marmar et al., 2006). Differences by gender and ethnic group have also been observed, although this is not consistent across all studies (Bowler et al., 2010; Bowler et al., 2012; Lilly, Pole, Best, Metzler, & Marmar, 2009; Marmar et al., 2006).

Longitudinal studies have reported significant relationships between traumatic incidents experienced at work and PTSD in police officers (Huddleston et al., 2007; Stephens & Miller, 1998; Maguen et al., 2009). Huddleston et al. (2007) found that police recruits who had experienced one or more on-duty traumatic events had PTSD scores 64% higher than recruits who had experienced no on-duty traumatic events. Robinson et al. (1997) found that any encounter with death was the strongest predictor for total PTSD symptomatology among police officers. Trauma experienced on-duty as a police officer was shown to be more strongly related to PTSD symptoms than trauma experienced while off-duty (Stephens & Miller, 1998). Also, in a case-control study of officers with and without PTSD symptoms, trauma severity was the only predictor of PTSD symptoms (Carlier et al., 1997).

In a cross-sectional study of Finnish police officers, Leino et al. (2011) reported positive associations between exposure to work-related violence and symptoms of psychological distress, and between threats by a deadly weapon and symptoms of distress. In Sweden, investigators found that officers who worked at the scene of a fatal fire experienced higher stress levels than those working at hospitals where the injured were taken (Renck et al., 2002). Police who were exposed to traumatic incidents have also been found to have higher levels of depression and anxiety (Hartley et al., 2007; Martin, Marchand, Boyer, & Martin, 2009). McCanlies et al. (2016) conducted a study on the New Orleans police department personnel that faced Hurricane Katrina. The authors found that police had extended working hours, loss of sleep, and austere living conditions. Fourteen percent of police personnel reported both depression and PTSD symptoms (McCanlies et al., 2014).

Officers with PTSD are also more likely to experience a number of comorbid psychological conditions, suicidal ideation, and a reduced quality of life (Maia et al., 2007; Sareen et al., 2007). Sareen et al. (2007) found that PTSD was associated with major depression, mania, panic attacks, agoraphobia, social phobia, and substance abuse. They also reported that PTSD was associated with high distress, high suicidal ideation, and poor psychological well-being (Sareen et al., 2007). In studies that have evaluated PTSD with indicators of poor health in officers, officers with PTSD were more likely to report more frequent medical appointments, more use of sick leave, and more hospital admissions compared to officers without PTSD (Maia et al., 2007; Martin et al., 2009). They were also more likely to report poorer health than individuals without PTSD (Maia et al., 2007; Martin et al., 2009).

Krysinska and Lester (2014), in a meta-analysis of fifty articles, concluded that there is an association between PTSD and suicidality, coupled with depression and the trauma conditions. Gradus et al. (2010) examined all suicide deaths from 1994–2006 using the Danish national healthcare and social registries, and found that persons with PTSD had 5.3 times the rate of death from suicide than persons without PTSD. In the largest study to date focusing specifically on PTSD and suicide, Conner et al. (2014) examined veterans from 2007–2008 ($n=5,913,648$) and found that patients with PTSD had a 1.3 times greater risk for suicide.

An example of how exposure to traumatic events may lead to suicidal ideation was seen in a study by Violanti, Castellano, O'Rourke, and Paton (2006). The study explored suicide ideation in police officers who worked in the proximity of the September 11, 2001 (9/11) World Trade Center terrorist attack. Data were obtained for a period of 4 years (2001–2004) from Cop-2-Cop, a statewide New Jersey confidential phone hotline provided exclusively for police officers and their families. Results suggested that calls related to suicide ideation increased from pre-9/11 through 3 years post-9/11 and that the risk for urgent care suicide calls post-9/11 increased 1.65 times more quickly over time when compared to pre-9/11 urgent calls. Forty percent of callers indicated changes in sleep, and 34% indicated changes in appetite. Symptoms included thought disturbances (i.e., more psychotic thinking including paranoia) in 10%, flashbacks in 6%, and nightmares in 5%, are serious and suggested more severe or acute forms of a mental health disorder.

DEPRESSION

Several studies on police have found the prevalence of depression to be approximately 12% among police (Hartley et al., 2012) which is nearly twice as high as the general population (6.8%; Reeves et al., 2011). This somewhat surprising finding may be attributed to a few key differences. First, age is a significant risk factor for depression. According to the National Institutes of Mental Health, adults 30-44 years of age are 120% more likely and adults 45-59 are 100% more likely to experience depression during their lifetime than those over the age of 60 (http://www.nimh.nih.gov/statistics/1MDD_ADULT .shtml). Over 90% of officers fell into these working age categories (Hartley et al., 2012). Depression has been strongly associated with suicidal ideation and behavior among police (Violanti et al., 2008).

Depression and PTSD are often found together in studies (Hodgson & Webster, 2011; Marmar et al., 1999). These disorders may have a cumulative effect over a police career. The Darensburg et al. (2006) findings suggested a significant difference in depression scores across age, with older officers having the highest depression and PTSD scores. The prevalence of depression was slightly greater among female than male officers. The prevalence of PTSD was slightly greater among older officers.

Depression has been associated with increased risk of cardiovascular disease (CVD) (Wang et al., 2010). Barefoot and Schroll (1996) found that a high level of depressive symptoms predicted the subsequent occurrence of myocardial infarction and mortality in a 21-year follow-up study. Appels and Mulder (1998) found relationships between various negative psychological states and the occurrence of coronary heart disease. Krishman et al. (2002) estimated that at any given time, up to 20% of persons with heart disease also met the criteria for depression. Depression has also been associated with biological outcomes which exacerbate the risk of CVD, including hyperactivity within the hypothalamic-pituitary-adrenal axis, diminished heart rate variability, and ventricular instability (Musselman et al., 1998). Hartley et al. (2012) found an association between components of the metabolic syndrome and depressive symptoms among a police sample. The number of metabolic syndrome components increased significantly across categories of depressive symptoms for male officers (p-trend significance = 0.003). For each 5-unit increase in the depression score, odds for having high triglycerides increased by 47.6%, 51.8% for having hypertension, and 56.7% for having glucose intolerance.

Police officers with PTSD or depression are at an increased risk for negative health issues such as cardiovascular disease and gastrointestinal disorders, comorbid psychological conditions as well as suicidal ideation and suicide (Gupta, 2013; Maia et al., 2007; Slavich & Irwin, 2014). Previous studies identified a significantly increased prevalence of the metabolic syndrome among those officers in the severe PTSD symptom category compared with the lowest PTSD severity category. Officers with severe PTSD symptoms were approximately three times more likely to have the metabolic syndrome which may account for this association (Violanti et al., 2006).

HOPELESSNESS

A sense of hopelessness may occur among police officers given the perceived futility of their work and work-related stress (Marmar et al., 2006). Faced with responding to fatal accidents, crime, child abuse, homicide, suicide, and rape, police officers are exposed to potential factors that precipitate a detrimental psychological effect (Carlier,

Lamberts, & Gersons, 1997). Violanti et al. (2016) examined associations between hopelessness, work stress, and PTSD among police officers. Lack of organizational support was associated with significantly increasing levels of hopelessness. Lack of support may be a source of hopelessness for police officers because they perceive them as unchangeable and beyond their control (Shane, 2010). Officers also comment that they are seldom acknowledged for doing a good job and more often cited for negative actions (Karasek & Theorell, 1990). LaRocco, House, and French (1980) reported that indicators of job stress and strain are directly affected by job-related sources of support. These authors add that support may help to facilitate cognitive reappraisal of work stress; therefore, alleviating negative self-blame (a factor involved in hopelessness).

Lack of support may also have a higher impact on levels of hopelessness for individuals with higher levels of PTSD symptoms. Violanti et al. (2016) found that in officers with higher levels of PTSD symptoms, lack of organizational support was positively associated with hopelessness. This result suggested that officers with high PTSD symptoms who perceive that they have little organizational support may become increasingly hopeless and potentially at higher risk for suicidal behavior. Support is crucial for those experiencing PTSD symptoms. Social support from family, friends, supervisors, and coworkers has been shown in repeated studies to attenuate or reduce the effects of psychological stress among police. Stephens and Long (1999) found that greater support and opportunities to talk about traumatic experiences and their emotional impact, with others in the workplace, were shown to be related to fewer PTSD symptoms among police. In a related study, Stephens and Long (1999) results suggest that a positive trauma-PTSD relationship was moderated by emotional support from police peers. Marmar et al. (2006) found that lower levels of social support were associated with increased PTSD symptoms. Martin, Marchand, Boyer, and Martin (2009) found that social support from police colleagues during the event emerged as a significant protective factor. Conner, Duberstein, Conwell, Seidlitz, and Caine (2001) suggest that hopelessness represents a psychological vulnerability and is an additional risk factor for potential outcomes such as stress, suicide, or depression in police work. These results suggest that hopelessness emerges within the social milieu and structure of the police organization and not in the danger of policing. Police organizations could consider further development of organizational structural factors to help increase support for stress, exposure to trauma, and the everyday work life of police officers. These are factors that are modifiable and amenable to change.

BURNOUT

Burnout is a syndrome consisting of exhaustion, cynicism, and diminished professional efficacy. Exhaustion refers to emotional exhaustion, and cynicism reflects an indifferent attitude toward work. Professional efficacy includes traits of occupational accomplishment and engagement (Leiter & Maslach, 2004). In the law enforcement environment, burnout may be seen as a response to the continuous and prolonged exposure to stress and is considered a serious health threat among police officers (Burke, 2017; Burke & Richardson, 2001). Reduced personal accomplishment involves directing these negative emotions toward oneself, resulting in feelings of inadequacy and a sense of failure. Studies on police burnout consider the impact of organizational stressors and work demands (Basinska & Wiciak, 2013).

A review study of burnout in policing (Burke, 2017) reported that police officers experience significantly high levels of (1) cynicism, (2) exhaustion, and (3) lower professional efficacy. Studies of burnout in policing report factors including: (a) high work demands together with lower resources (Martinussen, Richardsen, & Burke, 2007); (b) high demands as risk factor for higher exhaustion while high control resulted in greater professional efficacy (Hall, Dollard, Tuckey, Winefield, & Thompson, 2010); (c) organizational experiences of police officers being more strongly associated with burnout than operational experiences (Kohan & Mazmanian, 2003); and (d) attitudes about the use of violence (Kop et al., 1999). In a study conducted on Israeli police officers, the mean burnout score was found to be higher than the national average (3.05 vs 2.8) (Malach-Pines & Keinan, 2007). Other studies have found that burnout is associated with organizational and operational stress including lack of support from the community (Kula, 2017). The perception of danger at work and unfairness by the organization were also associated with burnout (McCarty & Skogan, 2012). Consequences of burnout can include substance abuse, decreased quality of service, and impaired mental and physical health. Research also indicates that burnout may be associated with dysregulated levels of hormones which may lead to physiological disease (Chida & Steptoe, 2009).

One of the prominent factors in police burnout is a high effort-low reward work condition. Siegrist (1996) developed a model for this called "Effort-Reward Imbalance" (ERI). ERI is based on social reciprocity, which is characterized by mutual cooperative investments based on the norm of return expectancy where a less stressful work environment depends on an equitable balance between efforts and rewards (Siegrist, 1996). Effort refers to the demands of the job, while reward consists of money, esteem, and job security (Siegrist, 1996). The reward structure depends highly on job stability, the prospect of promotion given a high level of performance, and a salary that is consistent with the work done (Siegrist, 1996). Additionally, it is important that workers feel a sense of esteem in the work organization and a cohesive relationship with the organization. The failure of a good balance of effort and reward elicit stress reactions (Siegrist, 1996; Siegrist et al., 2004; Siegrist & Li, 2016). Hence, numerous previous studies have associated the ERI model with stress at work (Lehr, Hilbert, & Keller, 2009).

In terms of the ERI model, police burnout appears to be associated with a frequent amount of work with little reward or support. The factors involved include high work demands, low resources, lower autonomy in making decisions, poor relationships between coworkers and supervisors, and other organizational experiences (Garbarino, Cuomo, Chiorri, & Magnavita, 2013). For example, in a sample of Canadian officers, higher levels of ERI were associated with greater psychological distress (Janzen, Muhajarine, & Zhu, 2007). A study conducted by Violanti et al. (2016) examined the association between ERI and burnout in police officers. Results suggested that ERI was positively associated with the burnout elements of cynicism and exhaustion. Increased levels of cynicism are nothing new in police research (Richardsen, Burke, & Martinussen, 2006). Organizational factors that have been examined in the police cynicism literature include job satisfaction, workload, and job resources. Within the context of ERI, Richardsen et al. (2006) found that the organizational factors of having heavy job demands and lack of resources were both directly related to cynicism. Overall, cynical officers have more negative work relationships, and those with more cynicism toward the police organization also report lower levels of job satisfaction (Bennett & Schmitt, 2002). Other research suggests that officers with higher levels of cynicism tend to feel more socially isolated than those officers with lower levels (Regoli, Crank, & Rivera, 1990). This emphasizes the important role of esteem, recognition, and appropriate feedback as indicated by the ERI model in reducing burnout-related cynicism.

Burke (2017) commented that burnout reduction is based on worksite changes and changing the orientation of individual officers by education and increasing personal resilience. Leiter and Maslach (2004) suggest reducing burnout with organizational changes which may increase the balance between effort and reward. They suggest reducing workload and increasing reward by allowing more control, acknowledging accomplishments, fairness, and financial balance. On the individual level, Leiter (1992) suggests that the selection process of new personnel should include an assessment of psychological and coping skills along with indoctrination training to help them to deal with stress and burnout. The author also suggests that individual counseling be available to assist workers experiencing work trauma and stress.

The recent movement toward positive psychology calls for an emphasis on increasing resilience among officers to ameliorate burnout. Resilience is considered as the ability to adapt successfully in the face of stress, adversity, trauma, tragedy, or significant threat (Horn, Charney, & Feder, 2014) and will be discussed further in Chapter 5. Resiliency can help officers resist burnout by rebounding from the negative aspects of burnout and to sustain the capacity to not be disrupted by stress and stay engaged at work. It is important to develop the leadership necessary to create a culture of resilience in policing. Leaders can increase resilience by increasing esteem of officers through participation in decision-making and positive feedback. In terms of the ERI model, this would allow some sense of control over work and increase self-esteem among officers.

EFFECTS OF ADVERSE CHILDHOOD EVENTS AND RETIREMENT ON POLICE MENTAL HEALTH

Aversive effects on mental well-being among police officers is not limited to service time. There may be factors which occurred in the

officer's life *prior to entering service and after the officer leaves.* There are
two dynamics outside of police service which may exacerbate mental
health in officers: (1) prior childhood abuse and (2) retirement from
police work.

Prior to Police Service: Adverse Childhood Events (ACE)

The CDC-Kaiser Permanente Adverse Childhood Experiences
(ACE) (Felitti et al., 1998) study is one of the largest investigations of
childhood abuse and neglect and household challenges and later-life
health and well-being. The original ACE Study was conducted at
Kaiser Permanente from 1995–1997 with two waves of data collection.
Over 17,000 Health Maintenance Organization members from Southern California receiving physical exams completed confidential sur-
veys regarding their childhood experiences and current health status
and behaviors (Felitti et al., 1998).

Adverse Childhood Events (ACEs) can have a profound effect on
the future well-being of individuals (National Center for Injury
Prevention and Control, Division of Violence Prevention. Centers for
Disease Control and Prevention (2019). An estimated 62% of adults
surveyed across 23 states reported that they had experienced one ACE
during childhood and nearly one-quarter reported that they had experienced three or more ACEs. (Merrick et al., 2018). ACEs can have
negative, lasting effects on health, wellbeing, and opportunity. These
exposures can disrupt healthy brain development, affect social development, compromise immune systems, and can lead to substance mis-
use and other unhealthy coping behaviors (Dube et al., 2002). The
evidence confirms that these exposures increase the risks of injury,
sexually transmitted infections, including HIV, mental health problems, maternal and child health problems, teen pregnancy, involvement in sex trafficking, a wide range of chronic diseases and the leading causes of death such as cancer, diabetes, heart disease, and suicide
(Chapman et al., 2004).

Figure 2.1 Effect of Adverse Childhood Events

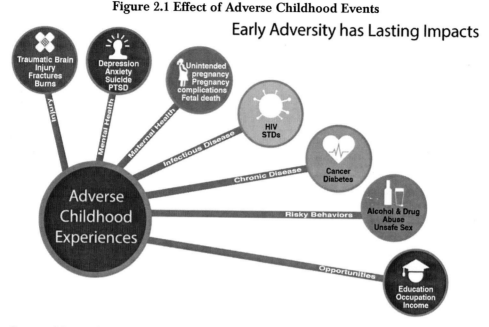

Source: National Center for Injury Prevention and Control, Division of Violence Prevention. Centers for Disease Control and Prevention (2019).

Felitti et al. (1998) found a strong relationship between childhood abuse and several leading causes of death. Fuller-Thomson, Baker, and Brennenstuhl, (2012) reported that childhood physical abuse was significantly associated with suicidal ideation. Dube et al. (2002) found a relationship between adverse childhood experiences and the risk of attempts at suicide throughout life. Angelakis, Gillespie and Panagioti (2019), in a systematic review found that all different types of childhood maltreatment including sexual, physical abuse and emotional abuse were associated with two- to three-fold increased risk for suicide attempts.

The Police and ACEs

Research is limited on the association of ACEs and the mental health of police officers. Once in police work, officers are further exposed to multiple trauma and stress. They see many of the evils of society, which includes the types of child abuse they themselves suffered. This can trigger trauma responses. In a previous study, seeing abused children was ranked as one of the highest stressors by police (Violanti et al., 2017). Exposure to child abuse on the job only further thwarts their sense of justice, leading to frustration and hopelessness. This may be especially true among sexually abused women officers who demonstrate a strong association between ACEs and hopelessness (Violanti et al., 2017).

A recent communication with police mental health professionals suggested that 25% of all police clients had a history of childhood abuse or neglect (Samuels, 2019). Many of those police clients also expressed suicidal ideation. ACEs experiences may exacerbate stressful or traumatic exposures of first responders such as police and lead to psychopathology. Studies on ACE among police and other first responders including firefighters and the military demonstrate negative psychological effects. Komarovscaya et al. (2014) did a study on first responders involved in relief efforts after Hurricane Katrina in New Orleans. Twenty percent of first responders who experienced physical victimization before age eighteen reported associations with symptoms of PTSD, peritraumatic dissociation, depression, and sleep problems. Otte et al. (2005) concluded that a history of childhood trauma in police is a profound predictor of post-traumatic stress disorder (PTSD). The ongoing study measured biologic risk in 400 police academy recruits and showed that 25% of the recruits experienced trauma before the age of 13 years.

In a presentation at the Anxiety Disorders Association of America (ADAA) 32nd Annual Conference, Dr. Charles Marmar (2012) expressed concern about child abuse among police and commented that

> A history of childhood trauma in police recruits who are without psychiatric symptoms is a "*profound*" (emphasis added) predictor of post-traumatic stress disorder (PTSD), 25% of the recruits in our study experienced trauma before the age of 13 years—a rate similar to that in the general population. . . . It could have been exposure to violence, a motor vehicle accident, abuse, and other causes. . . . I think the view is that this kind of information could be used not to exclude people from service but to provide resilience-building training and/or to triage people into different roles. . . . So in young, healthy recruits with no current psychiatric illness, the endocrine response is already upregulated if they have a history of childhood trauma. . . . If you have the genetic vulnerability and you're exposed to early

childhood trauma, you're predisposed to emotion dysregulation in terms of terror, horror, helplessness at the time of traumatic exposure, and that in turn predicts PTSD. . . . 16% to 17% of our sample is becoming more symptomatic progressively with cumulative exposure of every year of police service. . . .

Violanti, Mnatsakanova, Gu, and Andrew (2021) reported on ACE events experienced by police officers. Figure 2.2 provides types and frequency of adverse events graph, and Figure 2.3 compares the number of ACE events between police officers and the general public.

Figure 2.2
Type and % of Adverse Childhood Experiences Among Police

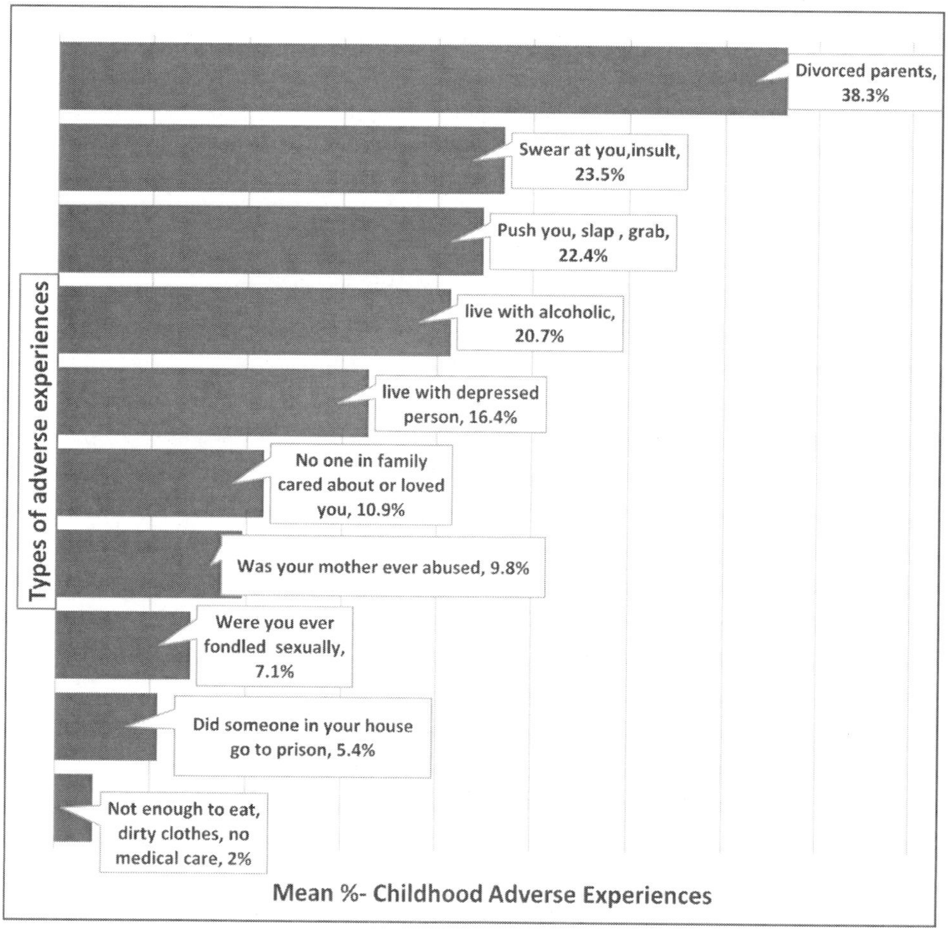

Divorced parents, 38.3%
Swear at you, insult, 23.5%
Push you, slap , grab, 22.4%
live with alcoholic, 20.7%
live with depressed person, 16.4%
No one in family cared about or loved you, 10.9%
Was your mother ever abused, 9.8%
Were you ever fondled sexually, 7.1%
Did someone in your house go to prison, 5.4%
Not enough to eat, dirty clothes, no medical care, 2%

Types of adverse experiences

Mean %- Childhood Adverse Experiences

Figure 2.3
Comparison of Number of ACEs Between General Population and Police

Number of Adverse Childhood Experiences (ACE Score)	Women		Men		Total	
	Police	Public	Police	Public	Police	Public
0	29.4	34.5	40.	38.0	37.2	36.1
1	19.6	24.5	27.3	27.9	25.1	26.0
2	11.8	15.5	13.6	16.4	13.1	15.9
3	13.7	10.3	9.9	8.6	10.9	9.5
4 or more	25.5	15.2	9.0	9.2	13.7	12.5

As seen in Figure 2.2 the highest reported rate of ACE was having divorced parents (38.3%). Being sworn at and insulted (23.5%) and being slapped or grabbed (22.4%) were the highest-rated adverse experiences. It was reported that 19.6% of female officers were sexually abused as children.

Figure 2.3 shows a comparison between the number of ACE events among police and those of the general public. Notably, a higher percent of police officers had four or more ACE event compared to the public (13.7% vs. 12.5%). The severity of future mental and physical problems increase as the number of ACE events increase (Herzog et al., 2018). Women officers were especially higher in 4 or more events than the public (25.5% vs. 15.2%), indicating a higher abuse ratio among women who become police officers.

Other first responder populations appear to have effects from ACEs. Hom et al. (2017) examined whether early life physical and sexual abuse was associated with suicide ideation and suicide risk in a sample of firefighters. Hom et al. (2017) found a significant correlation between early physical abuse and suicide risk in this population regardless of the danger and trauma they faced at work. Aronson et al. (2020) examined the relationship between ACE and combat exposure on the current mental health in a sample of recent military veterans. Fifty-nine percent of female and 39% of male veterans reported exposure to one ACE, whereas 44% of female and 25% of male veterans were exposed to multiple ACEs. ACEs were more consistently associated with mental health problems for male veterans than females. For males, a higher level of abuse was associated with probable PTSD and anxiety. Combat patrol events were associated with an increase in the likelihood of having a probable mental health problem (Aronson, 2020).

The ACE study included only 10 childhood traumas because those were mentioned as most common by the ACE national population group of 17,000 respondents (Felitti et al., 1998).

There are many other types of childhood trauma:

- Racism
- Bullying
- Watching a sibling being abused
- Losing a caregiver (grandmother, mother, grandfather, etc.)
- Homelessness
- Surviving and recovering from a severe accident
- Witnessing a father being abused by a mother
- Witnessing a grandmother abusing a father
- Involvement with the foster care system
- Involvement with the juvenile justice system, etc.

Additional abuses such as these only increase the risk of future mental health consequences. It is important for police departments to understand a potential candidate's childhood exposure to abuse at the entry level, as it may increase that candidate's risk for future mental difficulties and PTSD. Training in stress and trauma awareness should include information about helping officers understand how past traumatic life experiences may affect their work and well-being. Topics in wellness training should include the use of positive coping strategies to deal with exposure to child abuse and trauma on the job.

After Police Service: Police Retirement

Retirement is a significant life event for police officers. Leaving police work does not always reduce mental strife; often there are remaining vestiges of trauma and loss. The loss of police identity is difficult for officers. Although some officers eagerly await retirement, it signals the end of relationships and routine. The police subculture is a closed mini-society where officers maintain a sense of strong cohesion and dependence upon one another for survival. It is not easy for police officers to leave this interpersonal web of protection. Under such conditions, one would expect that retired officers would be more prone to mental issues. Police officers approaching retirement have the same concerns as other workers. Fretz, Kluge, Ossana, and Jones (1989) studied predictors of pre-retirement anxiety in individuals close to separation. Results indicated that the best predictors of pre-retirement anxiety were a low sense of self-efficacy, poor planning, financial insecurity, and bad health. The support of others appeared to help the retiree deal with impending mental stress.

Kea (1988) conducted a study which compared well-being among retired and active Los Angeles police officers and found that: (1) retired officers with low self-esteem reported less well-being; (2) retired officers who felt out of control of the situation also reported less well-being; and (3) officers who retired voluntarily had a higher level of life satisfaction than those who were forced to retire. Lastly, job satisfaction appeared to increase over time, with retirees being highest (in retrospect). Crowley (1984) examined the long-term effects of retirement on well-being and health. Using data from the National Longitudinal Survey of the Labor Market of Mature Men, she established five categories of retirees: voluntary-early age, voluntary-normal age, health retirement, mandatory retirement, and discouraged retirement. Voluntary retirees were found to consider themselves better off than did other retirees or those still working. The effect of retirement on well-being seemed to be related to many other factors besides the retirement itself. Most frequently mentioned by retirees were matters concerning finances and health.

Rank may play a part in adaptation to retirement. Because of the difficulty in obtaining rank in police work, position is often viewed as a symbol of status among officers. Rank comes with privileges: respect, authority, and prestige. The officer who retires as a captain or inspector likely has much more to give up than the street patrol officer. Initial levels of deprivation are apt to be more severe upon retirement for higher-ranking officers, but after initial adjustment they may actually be at an advantage in retirement. Dillard (1982) found that job rank influenced satisfaction more than retirement itself. Those in low status positions had less life satisfaction than those in higher status positions. Thus, higher-ranking officers not only enjoyed the benefit of additional skills for second careers, they also had greater life satisfaction than lower-ranking officers.

There are few officers who can retire from police work and not experience a sense of loss. Worden (1982) points out that after one sustains loss, there are certain tasks that must be accomplished before psychological equilibrium can be restored. First, the retired officer must accept the reality of the loss. Officers may try to protect their feelings by denying that they are no longer in police work. Statements like, "I'm glad to get out of the job," or "being a cop wasn't that important to me" by police officers are also attempts to deny the real meaning of the loss. Secondly, it is necessary to experience the pain of loss. If a retired officer continues denial, it may lead to psychological dysfunction. It is difficult for police officers who adapt the macho image to admit they feel pain. Third, the officer must learn to adjust to an environment without police work. The best way to deal with loss is to mentally redefine it in such a way that it benefits the new lifestyle. If officers dwell on the negative aspects of retirement, certain defeat will follow. Fourth, officers must withdraw emotional energy from police work and re-invest it into their new lives. If an officer retires and simply does nothing, he or she may soon experience depression. Most successful police retirees have in some way reinvested their energy into other activities. It does not necessarily have to be a job, but some sort of activity. This does not mean that one should abandon feelings about police work; it means that one should realize other things are worthy of time and energy. This, of all tasks, appears to the most difficult for retired officers.

The retired police officer should realize that adjusting to the loss of work takes time. There will always be memories of police work. One should accept them and set goals in other directions. Worden comments that grief may be finished when a person can think of a loss without pain . . . there is no longer that "wrenching quality" (Worden, 1982, p. 16) associated with memories. In a larger sense, however, one never completely finishes mourning over a loss. How one adjusts is the important factor. In essence, the retired police officer must integrate past history with present circumstances and accept feelings of loss. Refusing to deal with experiences successfully could lead to anxiety, withdrawal, depression, and fear.

The effects of experienced of trauma do not always end when police officers retire. The residual stress hypothesis proposes that prior trauma exposure leaves residual effects which are widespread, deep, and long lasting (Figley & Boscarino, 2008). Police officers spend much of their careers preparing for the worse. Training generally emphasizes the worst possible case scenario and prepares officers to deal with that event only. As a result, many officers become occupationally and personally socialized into approaching situations with considerable suspicion. This defensive stance towards life activities can become an obsession and a liability for officers (Gilmartin, 1986). As one result of learned defensiveness, it is not uncommon to find "action junkies" (Wilson, 1980)—officers who are addicted to risk behavior. Some officers become addicted to this excitement and cannot function effectively without it when they separate from service.

An interesting hypothesis by Gilmartin (1986) purports that adrenaline addiction may be a result of learned behavior. The interpretation of the environment as always dangerous may subsequently reprogram the officer's thinking and set into motion physiological consequences. This will be interpreted by the officer as a feeling of energization, rapid thought patterns, and a general speeding up of physical and cognitive reactions (Gilmartin, 1986). Gilmartin adds that police work often leads officers to perceive even mundane activities not from a neutral physiological resting phase, but from a state of hypervigilance, scanning the environment for threats. Once a hypervigilant perception set becomes a daily occurrence, officers alter their physiology daily without being exposed to any types of threatening events. Thus, officers may continuously be on a physiological high without stimulation (Gilmartin, 1986). Pole (2008) surveyed trauma-exposed retired police officers on a variety of demographic and psychological variables and found that sharing work-related matters with friends and family worked best in dealing with residual trauma. Pole suggests that integration with others in the lives of retired officers is an effective way for them to deal with leftover trauma.

The police organization can benefit officers about to retire by helping with the transition process to civilian life. Even in times of strained budgets, they have resources to provide services like retirement programs, counseling, job placement, and information. The least costly thing departments can do is to support the retiring officer. The significance of small things brings big results. One should not have to feel cast aside upon retirement, and the department should attempt to keep in touch with its retirees. Many organizations have annual meetings with former employees just to let them know that they care. It helps the retirees and builds morale among working personnel.

WHY DO MENTAL HEALTH PROBLEMS PERSIST IN POLICING?

A number of factors affect an officer's willingness to seek professional help for mental difficulties. These include law enforcement culture identity, stigma with counseling, and fear of reprisal by the department (Gilmartin, 1986; Vogel, Wade, & Haake, 2006; Wester et al., 2010). Jetelina et al. (2020) found four barriers among police regarding obtaining mental health services: (1) inability to identify when they are experiencing a mental illness; (2) concerns about confidentiality; (3) belief that psychologists cannot relate to their occupation; and (4) stigma that officers who seek mental health services are not fit for duty (Jetelina et al. 2020). The police culture expects officers to be detached, unemotional, in control, and investigative, so much so that instilling these attributes are often part of police training and even carry into the personal lives of officers.

Stigma—A Barrier to Care

Mental health stigma is pervasive in society and can be especially strong in police work. The police culture advocates strength toward problem solving without exception; those who are perceived as weak or unable to fulfill duties due to mental problems may be considered unfit for duty (Watson & Andrews, 2018). Officers feeling suicidal may prevent them from seeking help out of shame and fear (Rusch, Zlati, Black & Thornicroft, 2014). Officers may not only be stigmatized by others but also by themselves. Bathje and Pryor (2011) suggested that persons may self-stigmatize based on the idea that they are no longer capable to perform their work. In a systematic review and meta-analysis on first responder barriers to care and stigma, Haugen, McCrillis, Smid and Nijdam (2017) found that stigma was experienced by a significant proportion of first responders, which led to delayed presentation in mental health care.

There are strategies that can help to reduce stigma in police work. Training in mental health and coping techniques generally work well. Education is a key. Quite often departments will bring in "success stories" of officers who received help and are now doing very well. According to Burns and Buchanan (2020), the decision to access psychological help was guided by the amount of awareness officers had about how psychological problems would affect their work. Officers with little understanding of psychological issues were more likely not to seek help. The authors also found that support of supervisors played an important role in officers seeking help and successfully returning to work.

Soomro and Yanos (2018) "found that endorsement of negative stereotypes about people with mental illness was higher among police officers in general than among the general population." This may be attributed to police officers performing their job duties in the public eye. Endorsement of negative stereotypes suggests law enforcement personnel will have a more difficult time seeking mental health treatment. Soomro and Yanos (2018) suggested analyzing the role the gender of police officers plays in endorsing the mental health stigma. Current research is limited to identifying if gender is a variable that changes the way police officers feel about seeking mental health services or the behavior toward peers with mental illnesses (Pasciak & Kelley, 2013).

Police officers often comment that the organization is the biggest fear factor they face when considering help. Establishing trust between the organization and the working officer may alleviate much of the schism between the two levels. With trust, the police organization can help to reduce mental distress by fostering a sense of support and help officers overcome negative experiences and potential mental strain. Confidentiality is another a big issue. Police officers fear that supervisors will find out about their mental status. Education concerning mental health and effective treatment is needed for police officers. The stigma attached to mental illness and the reluctance of officers to seek help can only lead to further increases in mental strain and suicide among police. Policing is an essential occupation to preserve the rule of law and those who serve in law enforcement.

As outlined in this chapter, there any many dimensions of mental health issues that occur among police officers. Police officers are not immune to mental strife, and, further, mental well-being and wellness initiatives are needed by police organizations. In the long run it is the support of organizations that will make a big difference. In the next chapter, we move to the most tragic aspect of police mental strife: suicide. Suicide is an indicator of the intolerable strain of police work and life away from work.

REFERENCES

American Psychiatric Association. (2013). *Diagnostic and statistical manual of mental disorders* (5th ed.). Arlington, VA.

Angelakis, I., Gillespie, E. L., & Panagioti, M. (2019). Childhood maltreatment and adult suicidality: A comprehensive systematic review with meta-analysis. *Psychological Medicine, 49*(7), 1057–1078. https://doi.org/10.1017/S0033291718003823

Appels, A., & Mulder, P. (1998). Excess fatigue as a precursor of myocardial infarction. *European Heart Journal, 9,* 758–764.

Aronson, K. R., Perkins, D. F., Morgan, N. R., Bleser, J. A., Vogt, D., Copeland, L. A., . . . Finley, E. P. (2020). The impact of adverse childhood experiences (ACEs) and combat exposure on mental health conditions among new post-9/11 veterans. *Psychological Trauma: Theory, Research, Practice and Policy, 12*(7), 698–706. https://doi.org/10.1037/tra0000614

Barefoot, J. C., & Schroll, M. (1996). Symptoms of depression, acute myocardial infarction, and total mortality in a community sample. *Circulation, 93,* 1976–1980.

Basi?ska, B., & Wiciak, I. (2013). Evaluation of professional demands and financial reward through the perception of police managers. *Internal Security, 5*(2), 171–184.

Bathje, G. J., & Pryor, J. B. (2011). The relationships of public and self-stigma to seeking mental health services. *Journal of Mental Health Counseling, 33*(2), 161–177. https://doi.org/10.17744/mehc.33.2.g6320392741604l1

Bennett, R. R., & Schmitt, E. (2002). The effect of work environment on levels of police cynicism: A comparative study. *Police Quarterly, 5*(3), 493–522.

Bowler, R. M., Han, H., Gocheva, V., Nakagawa, S., Alper, H., DiGrande, L., & Cone, J. E. (2010). Gender differences in probable posttraumatic stress disorder among police responders to the 2001 World Trade Center terrorist attack. *American Journal of Industrial Medicine, 53*(12), 1186–1196.

Bowler, R. M., Harris, M., Li, J., Gocheva, V., Stellman, S. D., Wilson, K., . . . Cone, J. E. (2012). Longitudinal mental health impact among police responders to the 9/11 terrorist attack. *American Journal of Industrial Medicine, 55*(4), 297–312.

Burke, R. J., & Richardson, A. (2001). Psychological burnout in organizations: Research and intervention In R. T. Golembiewski (Ed.), *Handbook of organizational behavior* (2nd ed., pp. 327–364). New York, NY: Marcel Dekker.

Burke, R. J. (2017). Burnout in police work. In R. J. Burke (Ed.) *Stress in policing: Sources, consequences, and interventions* (pp. 154–169. New York, NY: Routledge.

Burns, C., & Buchanan, M. (2020). Factors that influence the decision to seek help in a police population. *International Journal of Environmental Research and Public Health, 17*(18), 6891. https://doi.org/10.3390/ijerph17186891

Carlier, I. V., Lamberts, R. D., & Gersons, B. P. (1997). Risk factors for posttraumatic stress symptomatology in police officers: A prospective analysis. *The Journal of Nervous and Mental Disease, 185*(8), 498–506.

Centers for Disease Control and Prevention. (2019). *Preventing adverse childhood experiences: Leveraging the best available evidence.* Atlanta, GA: National Center for Injury Prevention and Control, Centers for Disease Control and Prevention. https://www.cdc.gov/violenceprevention/pdf/preventingACES.pdf

Chapman, D. P., Anda, R. F., Felitti, V. J., Dube, S. R., Edwards, V. J., & Whitfield, C. L. (2004). Adverse childhood experiences and the risk of depressive disorders in adulthood. *Journal of Affective Disorders, 82,* 217–225

Chida, Y., & Steptoe, A. (2009). Cortisol awakening response and psychosocial factors: A systematic review and meta-analysis. *Biological Psychology, 80*(3), 265–278. https://doi.org/10.1016/j.biopsycho.2008.10.004

Conner, K. R., Bossarte, R. M., He, H., Arora, J., Lu, N., Tu, X. M., & Katz, I. R. (2014). Posttraumatic stress disorder and suicide in 5.9 million individuals receiving care in the Veterans Health Administration health system. *Journal of Affective Disorders, 166,* 1–5. doi: 10.1016/j.jad.2014.04.067

Conner, K., Duberstein, P., Yeates, C., Larry, S., & Caine, E. (2001). Psychological vulnerability to completed suicide: A review of empirical studies. *Suicide & Life-Threatening Behavior. 31,* 367–385. 10.1521/suli.31.4.367.22048

Crowley, J. (1984). *Longitudinal effects of retirement on men's well-being and health.* Paper presented to the 92nd Convention of the American Psychological Association, Toronto, Canada.

Darensburg, T., Andrew, M. E., Hartley, T. A., Burchfiel, C. M., Fekedulegn, D., & Violanti, J. M. (2006). Gender and age differences in posttraumatic stress disorder and depression among Buffalo police officers. *Traumatology, 12*(3), 220–228. https://doi.org/10.1177/1534765606296271

Dube, S. R., Anda, R. F., Felitti, V. J., Edwards, V. J., & Croft, J. B. (2002). Adverse childhood experiences and personal alcohol abuse as an adult. *Addictive Behaviors, 27*(5), 713–725.

Felitti, V. J., Anda, R. F., Nordenberg, D., Williamson, D. F., Spitz, A. M., Edwards, V., Koss, M. P., & Marks, J. S. (1998). Relationship of childhood abuse and household dysfunction to many of the leading causes of death in adults. The Adverse Childhood Experiences (ACE) Study. *American Journal of Preventive Medicine, 14,* 245–258.

Figley, C. R., & Boscarino, J. A. (2012). The traumatology of life. *The Journal of Nervous and Mental Disease, 200*(12), 1113–1120. https://doi.org/10.1097/NMD.0b013e318275d559

Fox, J., Desai, M. M., Britten, K., Lucas, G., Rosenthal, R., & Rosenthal, M. S. (2012). Mental health conditions, barriers to care, and productivity loss among officers in an urban police development. *Connecticut Medicine, 76*(9), 525–531.

Fretz, B., Kluge, N., Ossna, S., & Jones, S. (1989). Intervention targets for reducing preretirement anxiety and depression. *Journal of Counseling Psychology, 36*(3), 301–307, 1989.

Fuller-Thomson, E., Sohn, H. R., Brennenstuhl, S., & Baker, T. M. (2012). Is childhood physical abuse associated with anxiety disorders among adults? *Psychology, Health & Medicine, 17*(6), 735–746.

Garbarino, S., Cuomo, G., Chiorri, C., & Magnavita, N. (2013). Association of work-related stress with mental health problems in a special police force unit. *BMJ Open, 3*, e002791. doi:10.1136/bmjopen-2013-002791

Gilmartin, K. (1986) *Hypervigilance: A Learned Perceptual Set and Its Consequences on Police Stress.* 1–7. http://emotionalsurvival.com/hypervigilance.htm

Gradus, J. L., Qin, P., Lincoln, A. K., Miller, M., Lawler, E., Toft- Sorenson, H., & Lash. T. (2010). Posttraumatic stress disorder and completed suicide. *American Journal of Epidemiology, 171*(6), 721–727. doi: 10.1093/aje/kwp456

Gupta, M. A. (2013). Review of somatic symptoms in post-traumatic stress disorder. *International Review of Psychiatry, 25*(1), 86–99.

Hall, G. B., Dollard, M. F., Tuckey, M. R., Winefield, A. H., & Thompson, B. M. (2010), Job demands, work?family conflict, and emotional exhaustion in police officers: A longitudinal test of competing theories. *Journal of Occupational and Organizational Psychology, 83,* 237–250. https://doi.org/10.1348/096317908 X401723

Haugen, P. T., McCrillis, A. M., Smid, G. E., & Nijdam, M. J. (2017). Mental health stigma and barriers to mental health care for first responders: A systematic review and meta-analysis. *Journal of Psychiatric Research, 94,* 218–229. https: //doi.org/10.1016/j.jpsychires.2017.08.001

Hartley, T. A., Fekedulegn, D., Violanti, J. M., Andrew, M. E., & Burchfiel, C. M. (2007). Associations between major life events, traumatic incidents, and depression among Buffalo police officers, *International Journal of Emergency Mental Health, 9*(1), 25–35.

Hartley, T. A., Burchfiel, C. M., Fekedulegn, D., Andrew, M. E., Knox, S. S., & Violanti, J. M. (2011). Associations between police officer stress and the metabolic syndrome. *International Journal of Emergency Mental Health, 13*(4), 243–256.

Hartley, T. A., Knox, S. S., Fekedulegn, D., Barbosa-Leiker, C., Violanti, J. M., Andrew, M. E., & Burchfiel, C. M. (2012). Association between depressive symptoms and metabolic syndrome in police officers: Results from two cross-sectional studies. *Journal of Environmental and Public Health,* Article ID 861219. |https://doi.org/10.1155/2012/861219

Herzog, J. I., & Schmahl, C. (2018). Adverse childhood experiences and the consequences on neurobiological, psychosocial, and somatic conditions across the lifespan. *Frontiers in Psychiatry, 9,* 420. https://doi.org/10.3389/fpsyt.2018.00420

Hodgson, R. C., & Webster, R. A. (2011). Mediating role of peritraumatic dissociation and depression on post-MVA distress: Path analysis. *Depression and Anxiety, 28*(3), 218–226. https://doi.org/10.1002/da.20774

Hom, M. A., Matheny, N. L., Stanley, I. H., Rogers, M. L., Cougle, J. R., & Joiner, T. E. (2017). Examining physical and sexual abuse histories as correlates of suicide risk among firefighters. *Journal of Traumatic Stress, 30*(6), 672–681. https: //doi.org/10.1002/jts.22230

Horn, S. R., Charney, D., & Feder, A. (2014). Understanding resilience: New approaches for preventing and treating PTSD. *Experimental Neurology, 284,* 119–132.

Huddleston, L., Stephens C., & Paton D. (2007). An evaluation of traumatic and organizational experiences on the psychological health of New Zealand police recruits. *Work: Journal of Prevention, Assessment & Rehabilitation, 28*(3), 199–207.

Janzen, B., Muhajarine, N., & Zhu, T. (2007). Effort-reward imbalance, overcommitment, and psychological distress in Canadian police officers. *Psychological Reports, 100,* 525–530.

Jetelina, K. K., Molsberry, R. J., Gonzalez, J. R., Beauchamp, A. M., & Hall T. (2020). Prevalence of mental illness and mental health care use among police officers. *JAMA Network Open, 3*(10), e2019658. doi:10.1001/jamanetworkopen .2020.19658

Karasek, R., & Theorell, T. (1990). *Healthy work: stress, productivity, and the reconstruction of working life.* New York: Basic Books.

Kea, W. (1987). *Effects of locus of control, self-esteem and job satisfaction on subjective wellbeing in retired and active duty police officers in a metropolitan police department* (Doctoral dissertation). University Microfilms International, Ann Arbor, Michigan, 1987.

Kohan, A., & Mazmanian, D. (2003). Police work, burnout, and pro-organizational behavior: A consideration of daily work experiences. *Criminal Justice and Behavior, 30*(5), 559–583. https://doi.org/10.1177/0093854803254432

Komarovskaya, I., Brown, A. D., Galatzer-Levy, I. R., Madan, A., Henn-Haase, C., Teater, J., Clarke, B. H., Marmar, C. R., & Chemtob, C. M. (2014). Early physical victimization is a risk factor for posttraumatic stress disorder symptoms among Mississippi police and firefighter first responders to Hurricane Katrina. *Psychological Trauma: Theory, Research, Practice, and Policy, 6,* 92–96.

Krishman, K. R, Delong, M,, Kraemer, H., Carney, R., Spiegel, D., Gordon, C., . . . McDonald, W. (2002). Comorbidity of depression with other medical diseases in the elderly. *Biol Psychiatry, 52,* 559–588.

Krysinska, K., & Lester, D. (2010). Post-traumatic stress disorder and suicide risk: A systematic review. *Archives of Suicide Research: Official Journal of the International Academy for Suicide Research, 14*(1), 1–23. https://doi.org/10.1080/138111109034 78997

Kula, S. (2016). Occupational stress, supervisor support, job satisfaction, and work-related burnout: Perceptions of Turkish National Police (TNP) members. *Police Practice and Research. 18*(2), 146–159. 10.1080/15614263.2016.1250630

LaRocco, J. M., House, J. S., & French, J. R., Jr (1980). Social support, occupational stress, and health. *Journal of Health and Social Behavior, 21*(3), 202–218.

Leino, T. M., Selin, R., Summala, H., & Virtanen, M. (2011). Violence and psychological distress among police officers and security guards. *Occupational Medicine, 61*(6), 400–406. https://doi.org/10.1093/occmed/kqr080

Leiter, M. P. (1992). Burnout as a developmental process: Consideration of models. In W. B. Shaufeli, C. Maslach, & T. Marek (Eds.), *Professional burnout: Recent develop-ments in theory and research* (pp. 236–250). Washington, DC: Taylor and Francis.

Leiter, M., & Maslach, C. (2004). Areas of work life: A structured approach to organizational predictors of job burnout. In P. Perrewe & D. C. Ganster (Eds.),

Research in occupational stress and well-being (pp. 91–134). Oxford, England: Elsevier.

Lilly, M. M., Pole, N., Best, S. R., Metzler, T., & Marmar, C. R. (2009). Gender and PTSD: What can we learn from female police officers? *Journal of Anxiety Disorders, 23*(6), 767–774.

Maia, D., Marmar, C., Metzler, T., NÛbrega, A., Berger, W., Mendlowicz, M., . . . Coutinho, E. (2007). Post-traumatic stress symptoms in an elite unit of Brazilian police officers: Prevalence and impact on psychosocial functioning and on physical and mental health. *Journal of Affective Disorders, 97,* 241–245. 10.1016/j.jad.2006.06.004

Malach-Pines, A., & Keinan, G. (2007). Stress and burnout in Israeli police officers during a Palestinian uprising (Intifada). *International Journal of Stress Management, 14*(2), 160–174. https://doi.org/10.1037/1072-5245.14.2.160\

Marmar, C. R., McCaslin, S. E., Metzler, T. J., Best, S., Weiss, D. S., Fagan, J., . . . Neylan, T. (2006). Predictors of posttraumatic stress in police and other first responders. *Annals of the New York Academy of Science, 1071,* 1–18.

Marmar, C. (2012, April 17). *Risk and resilience biomarkers for depression and anxiety in police officers.* Paper presented at the Anxiety Disorders Association of America (ADAA) 32nd Annual Conference, Arlington, Virginia.

Martin, M., Marchand, A., Boyer, R., & Martin, N. (2009). Predictors of the development of posttraumatic stress disorder among police officers. *Journal of Trauma & Dissociation: The Official Journal of the International Society for the Study of Dissociation (ISSD), 10*(4), 451–468. https://doi.org/10.1080/15299730903143626

Martinussen, M., Richardsen, A. M., & Burke, R. J. (2007). Job demands, job resources, and burnout among police officers. *Journal of Criminal Justice, 35*(3), 239–249. https://doi.org/10.1016/j.jcrimjus.2007.03.001

Maslach, C., & Leiter, M. (2008). Early predictors of job burnout and engagement. *Journal of Applied Psychology, 93,* 498–512. 10.1037/0021-9010.93.3.498

McCarty, W. P., & Skogan, W. G. (2013). Job-related burnout among civilian and sworn police personnel. *Police Quarterly, 16*(1), 66–84. https://doi.org/10.1177/1098611112457357

McCanlies, E. C., Mnatsakanova, A., Andrew, M. E., Burchfiel, C. M., & Violanti, J. M. (2014). Positive psychological factors are associated with lower PTSD symptoms among police officers: Post Hurricane Katrina. *Stress and Health, 30*(5), 405–415. doi: 10.1002/smi.2615

Merrick, M. T., Ford, D. C., Ports, K. A., & Guinn, A. S. (2018). Prevalence of adverse childhood experiences from the 2011-2014 Behavioral Risk Factor Surveillance System in 23 States. *JAMA Pediatrics, 172*(11), 1038–1044.

Musselman, D. L., Evans, D. L., & Nemeroff, C. B. (1998). The relationship of depression to cardiovascular disease: Epidemiology, biology, and treatment. *Archives of General Psychiatry, 55,* 580–592.

Otte, C., Neylan, T. C., Pole, N., Metzler, T., Best, S., Henn-Haase, C., . . . Yehuda, R. (2005). Association between childhood trauma and catecholamine response to psychological stress in police academy recruits. *Biological Psychiatry, 57*(1), 27–32. https://doi.org/10.1016/j.biopsych.2004.10.009

Pasciak, A. R., & Kelley, T. M. (2013). Conformity to traditional gender norms by male police officers exposed to trauma: Implications for critical incident stress debriefing. *Applied Psychology in Criminal Justice, 9*(2), 137–156.

Pole N. (2008). Predictors of PTSD symptoms in police officers: From childhood to retirement. In D. Delahanty (Ed.), *The psychobiology of trauma and resilience across the lifespan.* Lanham, MD: Rowman & Littlefield, pp. 47–66.

Reeves, W. C., Strine, T. W., Pratt, L. A., Thompson, W., Ahluwalia, I., Dhingra, S. S., . . . McKnight-Eily, L. R. (2011). Mental illness surveillance among adults in the United States. *MMWR supplements, 60*(3), 1–29.

Regoli, B., Crank, J. P., & Rivera, G. F., Jr. (1990). The construction and implementation of an alternative measure of police cynicism. *Criminal Justice and Behavior, 4*(4), 395–409.

Renck, B., WeisÊth, L., & Skarbˆ, S. (2002). Stress reactions in police officers after a disaster rescue operation. *Nordic Journal of Psychiatry, 56*(1), 7–14.

Richardsen, A., Burke, R., & Martinussen, M. (2006). Work and health outcomes among police officers: The mediating role of police cynicism and engagement. *International Journal of Stress Management, 13*(4), 555–574.

Robinson, H. M., Sigman, M. R., & Wilson, J. P. (1997). Duty-related stressors and PTSD symptoms in suburban police officers. *Psycholological Reports, 81*(3 Pt 1), 835–845.

R،sch, N., Zlati, A., Black, G., & Thornicroft, G. (2014). Does the stigma of mental illness contribute to suicidality? *The British journal of Psychiatry: The Journal of Mental Science, 205*(4), 257–259. https://doi.org/10.1192/bjp.bp.114.145755

Sareen, J. et al. (2007). Physical and mental comorbidity, disability, and suicidal behaviour associated with posttraumatic stress disorder in a large community sample. *Psychosomatic Medicine, 69,* 242–248.

Shane, J. M. (2010). Organizational stressors and police performance. *Journal of Criminal Justice, 38*(4), 807–818. doi:10.1016/j.jcrimjus.2010.05.008

Siegrist, J. (1996). Adverse health effects of high effort/low reward conditions. *Journal of Occupational Health Psychology, 1,* 27–41. doi:10.1037/1076-8998.1.1.27

Siegrist, J., & Li, J. (2016). Associations of extrinsic and intrinsic components of work stress with health: A systematic review of evidence on the effort-reward imbalance model. *International Journal of Environmental Research and Public Health, 13,* 432–446.

Slavich, G. M., & Irwin, M. R. (2014). From stress to inflammation and major depressive disorder: A social signal transduction theory of depression. *Psychological Bulletin, 140*(3), 774–815. https://doi.org/10.1037/a0035302

Soomro, S., & Yanos, P. T. (2019). Predictors of mental health stigma among police officers: The role of trauma and PTSD. *Journal of Police and Criminal Psychology, 34,* 175–183. https://doi.org/10.1007/s11896-018-9285-x

Stephens, C., Long, N., & Flett, R. (1999). *Vulnerability to psychological disorder: Previous trauma in police recruits.* In J. M. Violanti & D. Paton (Eds.), Police trauma: Psychological aftermath of civilian combat (pp. 65–77). Springfield, IL: Charles C Thomas, Publisher, Ltd.

Stephens, C., & Miller, I. (1998). Traumatic experiences and post?traumatic stress disorder in the New Zealand police. Policing—An *International Journal of Police Strategies & Management, 21,* 178–191.

Strahler, J., & Ziegert, T. (2015). Psychobiological stress response to a simulated school shooting in police officers. *Psychoneuroendocrinology, 51,* 80–91. https://doi .org/10.1016/j.psyneuen.2014.09.016

Syed, S., Ashwick, R., Schlosser, M., Jones, R., Rowe, S. & Billings, J. (2020). Global prevalence and risk factors for mental health problems in police personnel: A systematic review and meta-analysis. *Occupational and Environmental Medicine, 77*(11), 737–747. doi: 10.1136/oemed-2020-106498

Violanti, J. M., Manatsakanova, A., & Gu, J. (2021). *Childhood abuse of police officers: Impact on future PTSD and depressive symptoms.* Virtual presentation, International Association of Chiefs of Police (IACP). Officer Safety and Wellness Symposium, March 17–22, 2021.

Violanti, J. M., Fekedulegn, D., Hartley, T. A., Charles, L. E., Miller, D. B., & Burchfiel, C. M. (2017). The impact of perceived intensity and frequency of police work occupational stressors on the cortisol awakening response (CAR): The BCOPS study. *Psychoneuroendocrinology, 75,* 124–131.

Violanti, J. M., Mnatsakanova, A., Andrew, M. E., Allison, P., Gu, J. K., & Fekedulegn, D. (2018). Effort-reward imbalance and overcommitment at work: Associations with police burnout. *Police Quarterly, 21*(4), 440–460. https://doi .org/10.1177/1098611118774764

Violanti, J. M., Castellano, C., O'Rourke, J., & Paton, D. (2006). Proximity to the 9/11 terrorist attack and suicide ideation in police officers. *Traumatology, 12*(3), 248–254. https://doi.org/10.1177/1534765606296533

Violanti, J. M., Charles, L., Hartley, T., Mnatsakanova, A., Andrew, M., Fekedulegn, D., . . . Vila, B. (2008). Shift-work and suicide ideation among police officers. *American Journal of Industrial Medicine, 51,* 758–768. 10.1002/ajim.20629

Violanti, J. M., Fekedulegn, D., Hartley, T. A., Andrew, M. E., Charles, L. E., Mnatsakanova, A., & Burchfiel, C. M. (2006). Police trauma and cardiovascular disease: Association between PTSD symptoms and metabolic syndrome. *International Journal of Emergency Mental Health, 8*(4), 227–237.

Violanti, J. M., Andrew, M. E., Mnatsakanova, A., Hartley, T. A., Fekedulegn, D., & Burchfiel, C. M. (2016). Correlates of hopelessness in the high suicide risk police occupation. *Police Practice & Research: An International Journal, 17*(5), 408–419. https://doi.org/10.1080/15614263.2015.1015125

Vogel, D. L., Wade, N. G., & Haake, S. (2006). Measuring the self-stigma associated with seeking psychological help. *Journal of Counseling Psychology, 53*(3), 325–337. https://doi.org/10.1037/0022-0167.53.3.325

Wang Z., Inslicht S. S., Metzler T. J., Henn-Haase, C., McCaslin, S. E., Tong, H., . . . Marmar, C. R. (2010). A prospective study of predictors of depression symptoms in police. *Psychiatry Research, 175,* 211–216.

Watson, L., & Andrews, L. (2018). The effect of a Trauma Risk Management (TRiM) program on stigma and barriers to help-seeking in the police. *International Journal of Stress Management, 25*(4), 348–356. https://doi.org/10.1037/str0000071

Wester, S. R., Arndt, D., Sedivy, S. K., & Arndt, L. (2010). Male police officers and stigma associated with counseling: The role of anticipated risks, anticipated benefits and gender role conflict. *Psychology of Men & Masculinity, 11*(4), 286–302. https://doi.org/10.1037/a0019108

Worden, W. *Grief counseling and grief therapy* (4th ed.). (2008). New York: Springer Publishing, pp. 1–30.

Wilson, J. P. (1980). Conflict, stress and growth: The effects of the Vietnam war on psychological development of Vietnam veterans. In C. R. Figley & S. Leventman (Eds.), *Strangers at home: Vietnam veterans since the war*. New York: Praeger.

Chapter 3

POLICE SUICIDE: WHERE TO BEGIN, HOW TO END?

It's not a sign of weakness to ask for help. It's a sign of strength.
—Unknown Author

Suicide is a public health problem. Nearly 47,511 people in the United States died by suicide in the latest available date (2019), making it the 10th leading cause of death. The age-adjusted suicide rate is more than 13.9/100,000 (American Foundation for Prevention of Suicide, 2020, https://afsp.org/suicide-statistics). In addition to other suicide risks such as psychiatric and life problems, occupation is a factor in suicide. Milner, Spittal, Pirkis, and LaMontagne (2013) found that the risk of suicide was greater among the least skilled or unskilled workers than in the general working-age population, likely due to lack of control over work. However, Milner et al. (2013) noted that there is also a higher risk for suicide in skilled professions. One such profession is law enforcement.

In today's societal and politically conflicted environment, the police are caught between the requirements of the job and the ability to fulfill these requirements. Negative public scrutiny, exposure to trauma, violence and mass murders, riots, unappreciated risks, sometimes risking their lives—coupled with any personal problems in living—all add up to the inability to cope. A sense of isolation results among police when it's coupled with frustration, pent-up aggression, and eventual depression fueled by exposure to trauma, death, abused kids, murder and human misery.

Officers die by suicide to escape the unendurable psychological pain brought about by work exposure. Jetelina et al. (2020) sampled police officers and their mental health status. Twelve percent of officers reported a mental health diagnosis, and 26% reported current symptoms of mental illness. Officers reported that they would be unlikely to seek mental health care because of lack of confidentiality, stigma, loss of job, and mistrust of mental health care professionals who do not understand police work. Bartone (2013) (Figure 3.1) provided an interesting taxonomy of suicide among military personnel. The structure of police organizations is similar to the military in many ways:

- *Enabling factors* make it easier for the individual who has decided to die by suicide to act. Enabling factors include easy access to firearms, alcohol consumption, and time of day when the suicidal person may be less visible to others.
- *Precipitating factors* are proximate causes. Precipitating factors include relationship problems or breakups, financial problems, disciplinary actions or investigations, job loss, and other stressful life events. For the person who is already at risk for suicide due to more basic or fundamental factors, such precipitating events can be enough to push them to a final act.
- *Background factors* are those variables that are associated with suicide, that are linked to increased risk for suicide without being specifically causative. This would include demographic variables such as age, sex and race, as well as history of mental health problems and violent or criminal behavior.
- *Formative factors* are fundamental ones that are the most likely cause of suicide. Feelings of hopelessness, depression, and social alienation are often seen in suicide victims.

Figure 3.1
A Taxonomy of Suicide

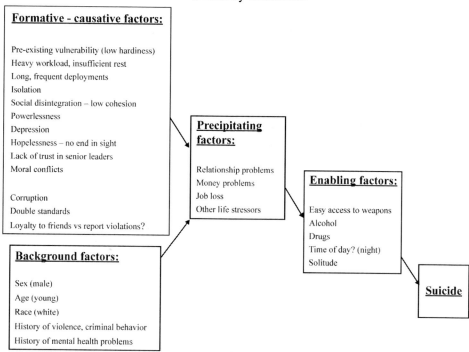

Source: Bartone (2013). Used with permission.

Violanti (1997), in an investigation of the potential for police suicide, commented that police workplaces persons into a restrictive role. Over time the police role takes a strong hold on the behavior of officers and they tend to use the police role in lieu of other life roles. Role restriction tends to negate other non-police roles that officers need in life and may leave the officer with no other way to cope with the stress of life outside of policing. Because of this role restriction, officers may be placed in a position of strain—not being able to "switch out" of the police role and deal with situations that require different coping strategies. According to Agnew (2001), persons in strained positions have problems reacting to a situation like this that push them in different directions, and they do not have the ability to cope with such strain.

Zhang (2005) proposed that suicide is a solution to situations of increased societal strain in individuals who feel alienated from the environment. This leaves them feeling cynical and isolated from society, which may exacerbate strain. In addition, a lowered level of societal integration associated with police cultural values may tend to isolate officers from the support they need in psychological crisis situations, increasing the risk of suicide (Arter, 2012). Violanti et al. (2018) found that social avoidance of non-police persons by police may affect the level of needed support during psychological crises support because it interferes with establishing a helping network. According to Joiner (2005) suicidal behavior may emerge in response to the strain of repeated exposure to physically painful and/or fear-inducing experiences—police officers frequently exposed to traumatic experiences and those who experience a sense of isolation from society.

NATIONAL STUDIES ON POLICE SUICIDE

Epidemiological evidence for increased police suicide risk has been found in three recent national studies. An early national study was conducted for the years 1984-1998 (Violanti, 2009), which were the only years available from the National Occupational Mortality Surveillance (CDC/NOMS, 2019) database at the time the study was done. The objective of this study was to examine national police suicide rates and compare rates with firefighters and military personnel. The NOMS database was used as a data source, and descriptive statistics and mortality rates were calculated. Overall, it was found the police suicide rate was four times that of firefighters but not as high as military personnel. Minority officers had 4.5 times and policewomen 12 times the number of suicides than did firefighters. The number of women suicides were small, and caution should be used in their interpretation. Police suicides outnumbered homicides by 2.36 times. Figure 3.2 represents the total number of suicides by year for police, firefighters and military personnel during this period of time.

Figure 3.2
Police, Firefighter and Military Suicides by year. CDC NOMS data, 1984–1998

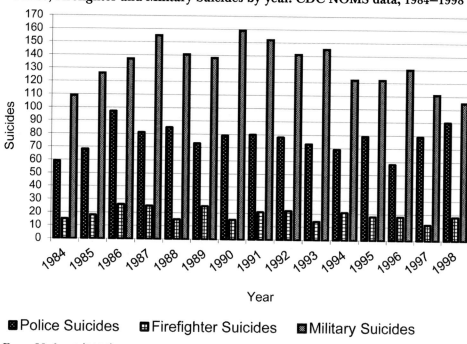

■Police Suicides   ⊞Firefighter Suicides   ▩Military Suicides

From Violanti (2009).

Data over the 15-year period (1984-1998) indicated a fairly level pattern of suicides across these three similar occupations. There appeared to be a slight upward trend in the number of police suicides in 1998 (*n*=90). Suicide in all three occupations decreased slightly in percentage across 15 years, however, the police had the least percentage of decrease. In the most recent five-year period (1994–1998) in this study, police had a slightly higher percentage of suicide than the other two occupations (32.6%, 30.7%, and 29.6%, respectively). Police work is generally considered dangerous because of the increased risk of homicide in this occupation. To explore this, we compared homicides, suicides and accidents to determine which category had the highest number of police deaths. Police accidents accounted for the highest percentage (51%) of deaths, followed by suicide (35%) and homicide (14%). This result suggested that suicide may impose a greater risk for death among police officers than homicide.

A second national study on police suicide was conducted in 2013 (Violanti, Robinson, & Shen, 2013) that compared police suicide to the U.S. working population. Using the CDC/NOMS database once again, the study looked at 1.46 million death certificates of workers who died in the 23 states that were the source of data. The study found 264 police suicide deaths over a three-year period which represented a 69% higher risk for police compared to all workers in the study population who were employed during their lifetime. White males had the highest number of suicides.

A third national study was conducted by Violanti and Steege (2020) that followed up the 2013 study, adding seven additional years from the updated NOMS CDC database. The study included all the latest data available from NOMS: 1999, 2003–04, 2007–2014 (11 years total). Death certificates for over 4.5 million deaths were examined from 26 reporting states. Findings indicated a significantly higher proportion of deaths from suicide for law enforcement officers (54% higher) compared to all U.S. workers in the study population. On average there were 100 police suicides per year over the 11-year period. The highest risk, as noted above, was for white males. A high risk was also noted for African Americans, Hispanic males and for white females. There was a slightly higher risk for suicide among police during the years 2007–2014, indicating an increase over previous years in the study. Although the *number* of deaths was lower in the higher (65–90) and middle age groups (46 to 64 years of age), those higher age groups had higher *proportions* of suicide than the working population in those same age groups (suicide, 94% higher and 46% higher, respectively) (Figure 3.3). In terms of age, the highest number of police suicide deaths ($n=484$) was in the 18–45-year age category, indicating mid-career officers (Figure 3.4). The results also suggested that law enforcement personnel in the western part of the United States had increased odds of suicide compared to other regions of the country.

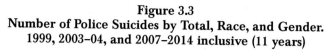

Figure 3.3
Number of Police Suicides by Total, Race, and Gender.
1999, 2003–04, and 2007–2014 inclusive (11 years)

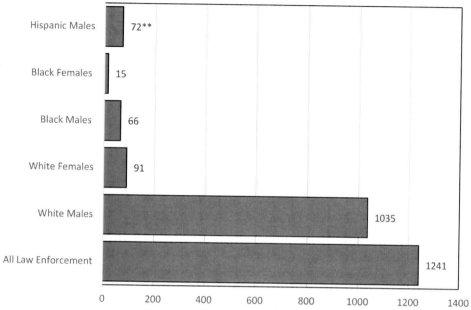

Note: Hispanic Female officers not shown. Categories with fewer than 5 deaths, or in categories allowing calculation of categories with fewer than 5 deaths are not available for publication.

Data Source: Violanti & Steege (2020).

Figure 3.4
Age Categories. Number of Police Suicide Deaths Over 11-Year Period.
1999, 2003–2004, 2007–2014

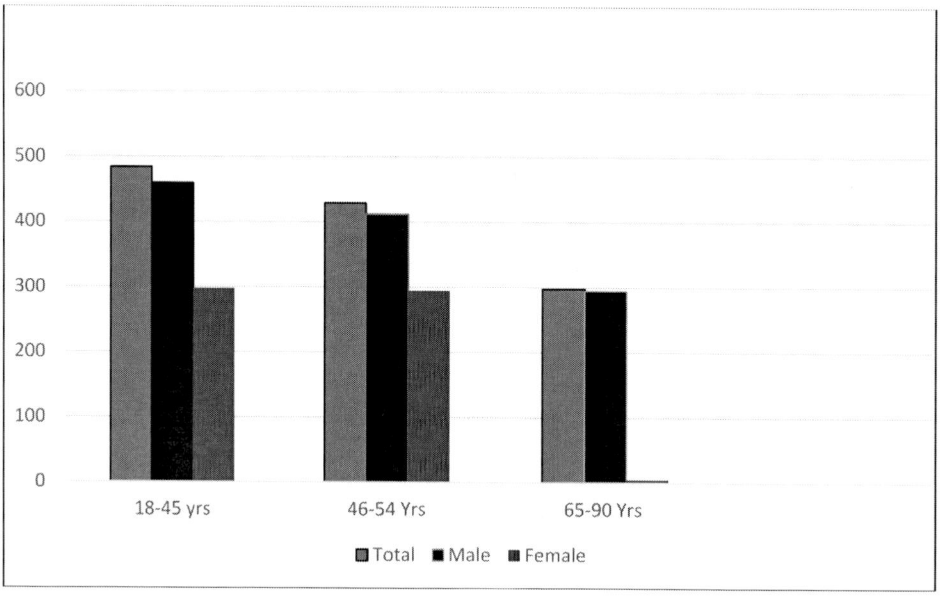

Source: Violanti & Steege (2020).

POLICE SUICIDE PREVENTION

Workplace suicide prevention efforts have focused on early detection and intervention through training on identifying risks for suicide and providing referral sources. However, more research in workplace suicide prevention is needed (Milner, Page, Spencer-Thomas & Lamotagne, 2015). Prevention of suicide specifically in law enforcement occupations warrants research that focuses on psychosocial and behavioral etiology. Thus far, knowledge about police suicide has been derived primarily from retrospective mortality studies, and less work has been done on suicide risk factors. Strategies such as implementing practices that encourage help-seeking, decreasing stigma, and educating employers about suicide are suggested. Stone et al. (2018) authored a Centers for Disease Control and Prevention (CDC) protocol for policy, programs and practices, a comprehensive approach to suicide prevention. These suggestions may easily be applied to police work. Further workplace prevention resources are available through the National Action Alliance for Suicide Prevention (Workplace suicide prevention, 2020, https://theactionalliance.org/), including examining the etiology of suicide.

At a recent suicide seminar held at New York City Police headquarters (NYPD, 2019) and attended by researchers and practitioners from all over the world, several suicide prevention themes were suggested:

- A central repository for capturing and analyzing suicide data is needed.
- Agencies should conduct psychological autopsies on police suicides.
- Agencies should mandate mental health checks to reduce stigma and normalize the focus on mental health.
- Police leaders need to speak out about the issue of police suicide within their agencies and in the community. Leadership from the top is crucial to getting this issue out of the shadows.
- Policies on taking firearms from officers who are seeking mental health service need development.
- Agencies should provide officers with training to help identify and support fellow officers showing signs of stress, depression or behavioral crisis.
- Agencies should offer confidential, easy-to-access tools (including online tools) for officers to assess their well-being and be referred to help, if needed.
- Agencies (especially small to mid-sized) should consider forming regional partnerships to help officers who may not feel comfortable approaching someone in their own agency.
- Following a police suicide, agencies should reach out to surviving family members and provide support, including assistance with any benefits issues and appropriate funeral honors.
- Agencies should devise a communications plan around messaging to the department and the public following a police suicide.

The International Association of Chiefs of Police (IACP) suicide prevention initiative (Brower, 2013) developed a national strategy to address police suicide prevention, built on the following four cornerstones: (1) culture change; (2) early warning and prevention protocols; (3) training; and (4) event response protocols. These proactive goals involved policy changes in police organizations and an acceptance that suicide is a real problem in this occupation. The chief obstacles to effective stress management programs include recognition of the need for stress services, the lack of empirical evidence indicating their benefits or effectiveness (for personnel and the agency), and the lack of funding to support such programs (Brower, 2013).

LOWERING POLICE SUICIDE RISK: CHANGING DYNAMICS

Stigma

Stigma refers to the process by which certain human characteristics are labeled as socially undesirable and linked with negative stereotypes about a class of individuals, resulting in social distance from or discrimination towards labeled individuals (Phelan et al., 2014). Stigma can be differentiated into enacted stigma, in which labeled individuals are treated differently from or denied opportunities available to non-labeled individuals, and felt or internalized stigma, in which labeled individuals avoid particular situations, interactions, or roles to prevent anticipated stigmatization, and/or endorse negative stereotypes about the group to which they belong.(Phelan et al., 2014).

An important finding by Jetelina et al. (2020) was that few officers seek mental health care because of the stigma associated with doing so. Stigma is one of the most frequently identified barriers to mental health care and is substantial among the police. Jayasinghe et al. (2005) found that after the September 11, 2001 terrorist attack disaster, slightly less than half of workers deployed to the World Trade Center accepted referrals for mental health treatment. Officers may feel that if they admit mental health problems and seek help, they will be less trusted by peers and supervisors to do their job and may lose opportunities for promotions. There is a need for more education for police concerning mental health and effective treatment.

As outlined by the U.S. Department of Health and Human Services (2006), many stigma reduction strategies follow a social marketing model. Social marketing is similar to traditional marketing but encourages behavioral change rather than purchase of goods or services. They offer recommendations for effective social marketing campaigns, including:

- Conducting a situational analysis to determine prevailing needs, attitudes, environments, and barriers.
- Developing and implementing a marketing plan, including selection of audiences and an implementation timeline.
- Convene partners and stakeholders early and throughout the process to help develop and implement activities and materials.
- Evaluating the effectiveness of the implemented strategies and refine as necessary.
- Investing both human and financial resources.
- Knowing your message, and emphasizing messages that are strength-based and focused on recovery.
- Developing a compelling and memorable theme.
- Watching your language, such as emphasizing "mental healthî rather than "mental illness."
- Establishing spokespeople, especially consumers of mental health services.

Corrigan and Penn (1999) described three broad categories of stigma reduction strategies:

- Protest: Protest highlights the injustice of stigma and leads to a moral appeal for people to stop thinking or behaving in stigmatizing ways. While research suggests that protest is not effective for changing underlying attitudes, it can be helpful in changing some behaviors.
- Education: Educational interventions emphasize replacing inaccurate stereotypes with new information. Even brief programs can lead to significantly improved attitudes about mental illness.
- Contact: Direct contact with people with mental health concerns also yields significant improvements in attitudes about mental illness.

Contagion

Contagion is defined as a group of suicides or suicide attempts, or both, that occur closer together in time and space than would normally be expected (Gould, 1990). A yet unexplored question is whether or not suicide contagion is more common among police than in the general population. It is possible that two influences may contribute to contagion in police work. First, through what Joiner (2003) terms "assortative relating," individuals who possess similar qualities or problems, including suicide risk factors, may be vulnerable to suicide as a group. The second influence may be the occurrence(s) of a suicide of a close coworker or friend who shares such relating. In short, Joiner's (2003) view is that suicide contagion is that a group of vulnerable people (in this case police officers) are cohesive and share stress via assortative relating. The stress may be the suicide of another officer or co-worker.

The New York City Police Department (NYPD) Chief Terence Monahan in 2019 made the statement that there may be a contagion of suicides among police officers after twelve NYPD officers died by suicide in a short time frame (Durkin, 2019):

> "It's really devastating," Monahan, the NYPD's highest-ranking uniformed official, said Tuesday in an appearance on WNYC's Brian Lehrer show. The officer was found dead at his home in Yonkers around 3 a.m., according to Yonkers police.
>
> "The number of suicides so far this year represents a sharp increase from the typical four or five a year," Monahan said.
>
> "Is there a contagion? This is something that psychologists and psychiatrists talk about—when one happens, there may be more," he said. The department is moving to hire more counselors and psychiatrists to work in precincts and to train cops to act as peer counselors for their colleagues.
>
> Department officials have been urging officers to seek therapy if they need it, seeking to dispel the stigma associated with mental health troubles among law enforcement.
>
> "We wanted to make sure we're putting this out [in the] open, to let our cops know it's alright to come and ask for help, to come forward if you have an issue in your life,î Monahan said Tuesday. "Get the help. If you're feeling that dark moment, get the help. . . ."
>
> No one cause has been identified for the string of suicides, but officials have pointed to the pressures of the job in combination with officers' constant access to a gun. Suicides have also ticked up among law enforcement officers nationally.
>
> "There are stresses of the job, complicated by stresses that you have in your own personal life, and compounded by the fact that you have a firearm on your hip,î Monahan said. "There are people who commit suicide in all walks of life that are in that dark place. We just want to try and get them out of that dark place and get them help."

Because of these recent suicides in the NYPD where a number of suicides occurred in a very short period of time and in a specific location, it is possible that this was a contagion effect. In theory, there are certain traits among police as a group which may facilitate a point suicide cluster effect. The police often view themselves as a family with strong comradery. This group cohesiveness may lead to close social integration and transmission among peers, acceptance of suicide as a solution, and assortative relating within close social ties.

The distribution of information through public or social media can affect contagion. In order to avoid possible contagion, police leadership must carefully consider on how they report the suicide of an officer. The Centers for Disease Control (CDC, 1988) made several recommendations for publicly reporting suicides, titled "recommendations for a community plan for the prevention and containment of suicide clusters in order to help prevent a contagion effect." The following is a summary of some of the recommendations:

- Do not present simplistic explanations for suicide. Cataloguing the problems that could have played a causative role in a suicide is not necessary, but acknowledgment of these problems is recommended.
- Do not engage in repetitive, ongoing, or excessive reporting of suicide in the news. Prominent coverage, of a suicide tends to promote and maintain a preoccupation with suicide among at-risk persons.
- Do not provide sensational coverage of suicide. Limit morbid details in their public discussions of suicide.
- Do not report "how-to" descriptions of suicide. Describing technical details about the method of suicide is undesirable.
- Do not present suicide as a tool for accomplishing certain ends. Presentation of suicide as a means of coping with personal problems may suggest suicide as a potential coping mechanism to at-risk persons.
- Do not glorify persons who die by suicide. Such actions may contribute to suicide contagion by suggesting to susceptible persons that society is honoring the suicidal behavior rather than mourning the person's death.

The CDC workshop also agreed that reporting suicide in the proper manner can have a positive benefit by promoting education about suicide, decreasing mental health stigma and getting professional help.

If suicide clustering is found to be more prominent in policing, police organizations can conduct education to make officers aware on how and why clustering happens. Additionally, organizations may adopt review committees on such suicides to aid prevention of future occurrences.

The Firearms Issue—"They Are Taking My Gun Away"

Can the possibility of suicide be lessened if the means are removed? There is considerable controversy as to the removal of firearms from officers who may be suffering from depression or contemplating suicide.

The Case for Removing A Firearm

On the one hand, police supervisors, out of caution and fearing possible suicide, will take firearms away from officers admitting suicidal ideation. Officers will then be placed on restricted duty not requiring a firearm such as desk duty. Possible evidence for removal of firearms:

- Studies suggest that restricting access to guns and reducing gun ownership can decrease the risk of firearm suicides (Kaufman, Morrison, Branas, & Wiebe, 2018). As an example:
- A meta-analysis (Anglemeyer, Horvath, & Rutherford, 2014) found that the risk of completed suicide was three times greater among persons with access to firearms.
- More suicides by firearm in handgun owners than non-owners (Kaufman et al., 2018).
- Laws and regulations that restrict access to guns are associated with decreases in firearm suicides (Mann & Michel, 2016).
- The risk of suicide increases in officers who live alone, have lost a loved one, or have experienced a failed relationship within one year (Buie & Maltsberger, 1989).
- The anniversary of a significant relationship loss is also a time of increased risk (Blumenthal & Kupfer, 1986).

The Case Against Removing A Firearm

Removal of an officer's firearm and placing the officer in a position off patrol has been dubbed being put in the "rubber gun" squad. Police officers place a symbolic meaning of identification with their firearm. Without it they may feel that they will be subject to ridicule and scapegoating by others. According to psychologists, another view is to allow the officer to keep a firearm because removing it will cause even more depression.

There are suicide prevention psychological protocols which can help to reduce the risk of suicide among persons having possession of firearms.

- Betz, Knoepke, Siry, Clement, Azrael, Ernestus et al. (2019) found that clinical efforts to highlight the high lethality of firearms (fear-based approaches) would be perceived by firearm owners as unacceptable.
- Studies suggest that emphasizing that limits to firearms are temporary might facilitate adherence to clinician advice (Stanley, Horn, Rogers, & Anestis, 2017). Thus, any removal should be *emphasized as temporary.*
- Stanley et al. (2017) found that emphasis on temporariness of firearm loss communicates to an officer that firearm safety interventions are not about "taking away guns" permanently.
- Making the environment safe: Give firearms to loved one to hold until things are better, Lock firearm in a timed safe so it is inaccessible for several hours after the crisis has passed; have loved one remove ammunition and place in a separate unknown location.
- Safety Planning Intervention (SPI) is a brief, six-step intervention that provides individuals with a written personalized safety plan to be used should a crisis develop (Stanley et al., 2018). Incorporating a lethal means safety intervention for firearms before the onset of an acute risk might have suicide prevention effects (Monuteaux, Azrael, & Miller, 2019).
- An SPI plan example provided to a police officer (Stanley & Brown, 2012):
  Step 1: Look for warning signs in me (suicidal thoughts, alcohol use, high stress)

Step 2: Things I can do to distract myself from thinking of suicide (exercise, movie, etc.)
Step 3: Situations and people that can help distract me (good friends, meetings)
Step 4: People I can ask for help if I need it (spouse, parents, other officers)
Step 5: Mental health professionals or other help I can contact (department psychologist, EAP, police peer support, suicide hotline) (Stanley & Brown, 2012).

Psychological Autopsies

Psychological autopsies have been suggested as a method to retrospectively examine the recent life of the officer who died by suicide to determine relevant factors associated with the suicide. A psychological autopsy can be defined as a procedure for reconstructing an individual's psychological life prior to the suicide to gain an understanding of what factors led the person to die by suicide (Maris, Berman & Silverman, 2000, pp. 66-67; Clark & Horton-Deutsch, 1992, p. 144; Cavanagh et al., 2003). The psychological autopsy obtains comprehensive retrospective information about victims of completed suicide (Beskow, Runeson & Asgard, 1990). A study by Brent, Perper, Kolko, and Zelenak (1988) showed that the psychiatric disorders reported in suicides also tended to aggregate in families. This finding was interpreted as a strong argument for the diagnostic data obtained by the psychological autopsy procedure being valid. Perhaps the best indicator of the reliability and validity of the method could be inferred from the consistency of findings across psychological autopsy studies (Brent et al., 1988).

Much of the data needed for a psychological autopsy can be found in a social history. Maris et al. (2000, p. 67) outline a list of possible sources of material:

- Psychiatric disorders of family members;
- Marital and psychosocial development;
- Education and employment;
- Present and past psychiatric illnesses;
- Hospitalizations and treatments;
- History of physical illnesses and injuries;

- Financial status;
- Religious affiliation;
- Family dynamics;
- Military history;
- Legal history;
- Socialization patterns;
- Previous attempts;
- Substance abuse;

We know little of the personal and life circumstances involved that led officers to die by suicide. In order to learn further possible precipitants of police suicide, the psychological autopsy is well established as the means for obtaining comprehensive information. The psychological autopsy obtains comprehensive information about victims of completed suicide (Robins et al., 1959; Beskow et al., 1990). A study by Brent et al. (1988) showed that the psychiatric disorders reported in suicides also tended to aggregate in families. This finding was interpreted as a strong argument for the diagnostic data obtained by the psychological autopsy procedure being valid. Perhaps the best indicator of the reliability and validity of the method could be inferred from the consistency of findings across psychological autopsy studies (Brent et al., 1988).

There has been little published on using psychological autopsies to examine police suicides. Rouse et al. (2015) used the psychological autopsy technique to examine the etiology of eight law enforcement suicides. Findings indicated that all officers had suicide risk factors similar to the general population. However, risk factors prior to employment as a police officer or on-duty traumatic events were not primary reasons for suicide in policing. A psychological autopsy study done by Encrenaz et al. (2016) on French police described life trajectories of police suicide. In more than half of the cases, police officers used their service weapon. Findings indicated that the majority of suicide were male and were suffering from depression. A second main cause was marital difficulties. The study called for pre-occupational screening of police officers and an increase in organizational support for troubled officers. Herndon (2001) examined behavioral patterns and the pre-employment psychological profile of a small sample of police officers who died by suicide and compared them with officers who threatened suicide. Psychological autopsy data showed that offi-

cers who completed suicide were higher in scores for hysteria, paranoia, and schizophrenia. Poor coping skills, job stress, loss of a loved
one, criminal charges, and organizational pressure were also noted in
those officers who died by suicide.

Post Suicide Considerations

The question often arises as to what should be done after a suicide
occurs in a department. The present guide offers sound advice on policy suggestions concerning this topic. Suicide post-event responses are
generally called "postvention." It is a shortened term for a post intervention after a suicide death and includes psychological first-aid and
crisis intervention. Many mental health professionals have stated that
postvention is really suicide prevention, as it may prevent future suicides by containing the crisis and lessening the chances for suicide
contagion in close-knit groups like policing.

Police leadership plays a critical role in postvention. Given the
serious nature of a suicide death and the disturbing aftereffects on
family, friends, other officers, and the department, it is imperative that
police leaders understand what to do should a suicide occur in their
jurisdiction. There are many questions to be answered. For example,
are death notifications different for suicides? How does a leader address the media response to the suicide? Will the funeral protocol be
different? How will the department care for survivors? Should officers
in the department be debriefed and/or referred to a health professional if needed? Is there a possible danger of contagion where other
officers may die by suicide? Leadership relying on an informal, un-
written policy is not a prudent approach given the scrutiny police face
and the potentially harmful effects of critical media coverage among
other potential effects.

The Workplace Postvention Task Force of the American Association of Suicidology and The Workplace Task Force of the National
Action Alliance for Suicide Prevention in partnership with the Carson
J. Spencer Foundation and Crisis Care Network in a publication titled
Manager's Guide to Suicide Postvention in the Workplace (2013) described
three phases that police leaders may follow to help alleviate the aftereffects of suicide:

Immediate: Acute Phase

- Coordinate: Contain the crisis (*very important!*)
- Notify: Protect and respect the privacy rights of the deceased employee and their loved ones during death notification.
- Communicate: Reduce the potential for contagion.
- Support: Offer practical assistance to family.

Short-Term: Recovery Phase

- Link: Identify and link impacted employees to additional support resources and refer those most affected to professional mental health services.
- Comfort: Support, comfort, and promote healthy grieving of the employees who have been impacted by the loss.
- Restore: Restore equilibrium and optimal functioning in the workplace.
- Lead: Build and sustain trust and confidence in organizational leadership.

Longer-Term: Reconstructing Phase

- Honor: Prepare for anniversary reactions and other milestone dates.
- Sustain: Transition postvention to suicide prevention.

Police leaders might consider additional policy decisions:

- Leaders should specify personnel responsible for the suicide post event (supervision, peer support, psychological services, clergy).
- A departmental communication release should be made as soon as is possible to dispel rumors and incorrect information.
- Conduct a debriefing and a follow-up session.
- Evaluate the post-event policy to address problems and improvements.
- Police leaders should understand that they will also experience grief from the suicide, and they may be the focus of anger and unjustly blamed for the death by other officers.

- Leaders should consider anniversaries and other major dates that might trigger reactions and which it might be appropriate to acknowledge the loss of that officer.

Suicide Survivors

Unfortunately, a suicide leaves behind many survivors. An estimated quarter million people each year become suicide survivors (https://save.org/about-suicide/suicide-facts/). This figure is likely an underestimation, as it may not account for the emergency responders, health care providers, coworkers, and acquaintances also affected by the suicide. Individuals who are closely related to the deceased are usually those most adversely affected by the death (Mitchell et al., 2009).

It is often said that police work is a close-knit cohesive occupation. Police officers consider themselves a part of a family. When an officer dies by suicide, other officers feel as though they have lost a brother or sister. In a sense, the officers in the department and the immediate family together grieve the loss. The grief response associated with suicide is different. Feelings of loss are often magnified in suicide survivors by feelings of guilt, confusion, rejection, shame, anger, and the effects of stigma and trauma. Furthermore, survivors of suicide loss are at higher risk of developing major depression, post-traumatic stress disorder, and suicidal behaviors, as well as a prolonged form of grief called *complicated grief.* Added to the burden is the substantial stigma, which can keep survivors away from much needed support and healing resources (Young et al., 2012).

In conclusion, a priority should be police suicide prevention, moving toward zero suicides in policing. Until we can obtain additional credible and accurate information on police suicide obtained and verified by police departments across the U.S., we must continue to estimate the true scope of this problem. Looking to the future, the development of proposed legislation for a recent national database specifically focused on police suicide would help to establish the actual scope of this tragic loss of life. Further research in the etiology of police suicide will help us to more effectively prevent these tragic and unnecessary deaths.

In the next chapter, the effect of mental stress and trauma on police health outcomes is explored. Chronic stress affects a number of systems throughout the human body, including the immune system, brain, cardiovascular, and digestive system, and is associated with a number of diseases in these systems.

REFERENCES

Agnew, R. (2001). Building on the foundation of general strain theory: Specifying the types of strain most likely to lead to crime and delinquency. *Journal of Research in Crime and Delinquency, 38*(4), 319–361.

American Foundation for Suicide Prevention. (2020). https://afsp.org/suicide -statistics

Anglemyer, A., Horvath, T., & Rutherford, G. (2014). The accessibility of firearms and risk for suicide and homicide victimization among household members: A systematic review and meta-analysis. *Annals of Internal Medicine, 160*(2), 101–110. https://doi.org/10.7326/M13-1301

Arter, M. L. (2012). Applying general strain theory to policing: Examining police stress In L. Territo & J. D. Sewell (Eds.), *Stress management in law enforcement* (3rd ed.). Durham, NC: Carolina Academic Press, pp. 71–103.

Bartone, P. T. (2013). A new taxonomy for understanding factors leading to suicide in the military. *International Journal of Emergency Mental Health and Human Resilience, 15*(4), 299–306.

Beskow, J., Runeson, B., & Asgard, U. (1990). Psychological autopsies: Methods and ethics. *Suicide and Life-Threatening Behavior, 20*(4), 307–323.

Betz, M. E., Knoepke, C. E., Siry, B., Clement, A., Azrael, D., Ernestus, S., & Matlock, D. D. (2019). "Lock to live": Development of a firearm storage decision aid to enhance lethal means counselling and prevent suicide. *Injury Prevention: Journal of the International Society for Child and Adolescent Injury Prevention, 25*(Suppl 1), i18–i24. https://doi.org/10.1136/injuryprev-2018-042944

Brent, D. A., Perper, J. A., Kolko, D. J., & Zelenak, J. (1988). The psychological autopsy: Methodological considerations for the study of adolescent suicide. *Journal of the American Academy of Child & Adolescent Psychiatry, 27*(3), 362–366. https://doi.org/10.1097/00004583-198805000-00016

Brower, J. (2013). *Review and input of correctional officer wellness & safety literature review.* OJP Diagnostic Center. Office of Justice Programs.

CDC Recommendations for a Community Plan for the Prevention and Containment of Suicide Clusters. (1988). *MMWR Supplements,* (August 19, 1988), 37(S-6), 1–12.

Clark, D. C., & Horton-Deutsch, S. L. (1992). Assessment in absentia: The value of the psychological autopsy method for studying antecedents of suicide and predicting future suicides. In R. W. Maris, A. L. Berman, J. T. Maltsberger & R. I. Rufit (Eds.), *The assessment and prediction of suicide* (pp. 144–182). New York: Guilford Press.

Corrigan, P. W., & Penn, D. L. (1999). Lessons from social psychology on discrediting psychiatric stigma. *American Psychologist, 54*(9), 765–776. https://doi.org/10 .1037/0003-066X.54.9.765

Cavanagh, J. T. 0., Carson, A. J., Sharpe, M., & Lawrie, S. M. (2003). Psychological autopsy studies of suicide: A systematic review. *Psychological Medicine, 33*(3), 395–405.

Durkin, E. (2019). NYPD chief calls spate of suicides 'devastating' after officers die. https://www.politico.com/states/new-york/albany/story/2019/08/13/nypd-chief-calls-spate-of-suicides-devastating-after-8th-officer-dies-1140203

Encrenaz, G., Miras, A., Contrand, B., Segiun, M., Muolki, M.Queinic, R. (2016). Suicide among the French National Police forces: Implication of life events and life trajectories. *Encephale, 42*(4), 304–313. doi: 10.1016/j.encep.2015.08.004. Epub 2015 Dec 10.

Gould, M. S. (1990). Suicide clusters and media exposure. In S. Blumenthal & D. Kupfer (Eds.), *Suicide over the life cycle: Risk factors, assessment, and treatment of suicidal patients*. Washington, DC: American Psychiatric Association, pp. 517–532.

Herndon, J. S. (2001). Law enforcement suicide: Psychological autopsies and psychometric traces. In D. C. Sheehan & J. I. Warren (Eds.), *Suicide and law enforcement* (pp. 223–233). Washington, D.C. U.S. Dept. of Justice.

Jayasinghe N., Giosan C., Evans, S., Spielman L., & Difede, J. (2008). Anger and posttraumatic stress disorder in disaster relief workers exposed to the September 11, 2001 World Trade Center disaster: One-year follow-up study. *Journal of Nervous & Mental Disease, 196,* 844–846. doi: 10.1097/NMD.0b013e31818b492c

Jetelina K. K., Molsberry R. J., Gonzalez, J. R., Beauchamp, A. M., & Hall, T. (2020). Prevalence of mental illness and mental health care use among police officers. *JAMA Network Open, 3*(10), e2019658. doi:10.1001/jamanetworkopen.2020.19658.

Joiner, T. E., Jr. (2003). Contagion of suicidal symptoms as a function of assortative relating and shared relationship stress in college roommates. *Journal of Adolescence, 26*(4), 495–504. https://doi.org/10.1016/s0140-1971(02)00133-1

Kaufman, E. J., Morrison, C. N., Branas, C. C., & Wiebe, D. J. (2018). State firearm laws and interstate firearm deaths from homicide and suicide in the United States: A Cross-sectional analysis of data by county. *JAMA Internal Medicine, 178*(5), 692–700. https://doi.org/10.1001/jamainternmed.2018.0190

Manager's Guide to Suicide Postvention in the Workplace: 10 Action Steps for Dealing with the Aftermath of Suicide. https://www.sprc.org/resources-programs/managers-guide-suicide-postvention-workplace-10-action-steps-dealing-aftermath. Accessed 3-29-21.

Mann, J. J., & Michel, C. A. (2016). Prevention of firearm suicide in the United States: What works and what is possible. *The American Journal of Psychiatry, 173*(10), 969–979. https://doi.org/10.1176/appi.ajp.2016.16010069

Maris, R. W., Berman, A. L., & Silverman, M. M. (2000). *Comprehensive textbook of suicidology* (p. 67). New York: Guilford Press.

Milner, A., Spittal, M. J., Pirkis, J., & LaMontagne, A. D. (2013). Suicide by occupation: systematic review and meta-analysis. *The British Journal of Psychiatry: The Journal of Mental Science, 203*(6), 409–416. https://doi.org/10.1192/bjp.bp.113.128405

Milner, A., Page, K., Spencer-Thomas, S., & Lamotagne, A. D. (2015). Workplace suicide prevention: A systematic review of published and unpublished activities. *Health Promotional International, 30,* 29–37. https://doi.org/10.1093/heapro/au085

Mitchell, A. M., Sakraida, T. J., Kim, Y., Bullian, L., & Chiappetta, L. (2009). Depression, anxiety and quality of life in suicide survivors: A comparison of close and distant relationships. *Archive of Psychiatric Nursing, 23*(1), 2–10.

Monuteaux, M. C., Azrael, D., & Miller, M. (2019). Association of increased safe household firearm storage with firearm suicide and unintentional death among US youths. *JAMA Pediatrics, 173*(7), 657–662. https://doi.org/10.1001/jamapediatrics.2019.1078

National Occupational Mortality Surveillance (NOMS). (2019). https://www.cdc.gov/niosh/topics/noms/default.html.

Reducing stigma. (2019). U.S. Department of Health and Human Services (2006). https://www.cdc.gov/coronavirus/2019-ncov/daily-life-coping/reducing-stigma.html

Robins, E., Murphy, G. E., Wilkinson, R. H., Jr., Gassner, S., & Kayes, J. (1959). Some clinical considerations in the prevention of suicide based on a study of 134 successful suicides. *American Journal of Public Health Nations Health, 49*(7), 888–899.

Rouse, L. M., Frey, R. A., LÛpez, M., Wohlers, H., Xiong, I., Llewellyn, K., Lucci, S. P., & Wester, S. R. (2015). Discerning etiology through psychological autopsy. *Police Quarterly, 18*(1), 79–108.

Schneidman, E. S. (1972). Foreword to A. C. Cain (Ed.), *Survivors of suicide.* Springfield, IL: Charles C Thomas, Publisher.

Stanley, B., & Brown, G. K. (2012). Safety planning intervention: A brief intervention to mitigate suicide risk. *Cognitive and Behavioral Practice, 19,* 256–264.

Stanley, I. H., Hom, M. A., Rogers, M. L., Anestis, M. D., & Joiner, T. E. (2017). Discussing firearm ownership and access as part of suicide risk assessment and prevention: "Means safety" versus "means restriction." *Archives of Suicide Research, 21*(2), 237–253. 10.1080/13811118.2016.1175395

Stanley, B., Brown, G. K., Brenner, L. A., Galfalvy, H. C., Currier, G. W., Knox, K. L., . . . Chaudhury, S. R. (2018). Comparison of the safety planning intervention with follow-up vs usual care of suicidal patients treated in the emergency department. *JAMA Psychiatry, 75*(9), 894–900. https://doi.org/10.1001/jamapsychiatry.2018.1776

Stone, D. M., Simon, T. R., & Fowler, K. A. (2018). Vital signs: Trends in state suicide rates—United States, 1999–2016 and circumstances contributing to suicide—27 states, 2015. *MMWR Morbidity Mortality Weekly Report, 67,* 617–624. doi: http://dx.doi.org/10.15585/mmwr.mm6722a1

Suicide Facts (https://save.org/about-suicide/suicide-facts/). Accessed 3-30-21.

Suicide Prevention Resource Center. (2013). *A manager's guide to suicide postvention in the workplace: 10 action steps for dealing with the aftermath of suicide.* https://www.sprc.org/

Occupation Under Siege

Violanti, J. M. (1997). Suicide and the police role: a psychosocial model. *Policing: An International Journal of Police Strategies & Management, 20*(4), 698–715. https://doi.org/10.1108/13639519710368107.

Violanti, J. M. (2010). Police suicide: A national comparison with fire-fighter and military personnel. *Policing: An International Journal of Police Strategies & Management, 33,* 270–286. 10.1108/13639511011044885.

Violanti, J. M., Robinson, C. F., & Shen, R. (2013). Law enforcement suicide: A national analysis. *International Journal of Emergency Mental Health, 15*(4), 289–297.

Violanti, J. M., Ma, C. C., Gu, J. K., Fekedulegn, D., Manatsakanova, A., & Andrew, M. E. (2018). Social avoidance in policing: Associations with cardiovascular disease and the role of social support. *Policing: An International Journal of Police Strategies and Management, 421*(5), 539–549.

Violanti, J. M., & Steege, A. (2020). Law enforcement worker suicide: An updated national assessment. *Policing: An International Journal, 44*(1), 18--31.

Workplace Suicide Prevention and Postvention. (2020). https://theactionalliance.org/

Young, M. B., & Erickson, C. A. (1988). Cultural impediments to recovery: PTSD in contemporary *America. Journal of Traumatic Stress, 1*(4), 431–443.

Zhang, J. (2005). Conceptualizing a strain theory of suicide (review). *Chinese Mental Health Journal, 19*(3), 778–782.

Chapter 4

POLICE STRESS AND TRAUMA: PHYSICAL HEALTH CONSEQUENCES

PTSD is a whole-body tragedy, an integral human event of enormous proportions with massive repercussions.

—Susan Pease Banitt

INTRODUCTION

This chapter discusses the effects of police stressors and trauma on health outcomes. Stress and trauma can eventually wear down the body's defense against disease. With the present-day intensification of stress on police, we may see increasing health problems among police. Chronic stress affects a number of systems throughout the human body, including the immune system, brain, cardiovascular, and digestive system, and is associated with a number of diseases in these systems (Nagaraja et al., 2016). Stress and heart disease are associated. Heart disease including stroke cost the United States approximately $191 billion each year, diabetes over $327 billion in medical costs and lost productivity, and cancer over $174 billion in 2020 (CDC, 2020). Calculations by the Commission on Accreditation for Law Enforcement estimated that the cost of a police in-service heart attack ranged between $450,000–$750,000, accounting for medical expenses, duty time lost, and replacement of the officer while in recovery (Smith & Tooker, 2005). These figures do not account for other psychological or biological disorders experienced by police officers as a result of the stress they experience.

Mental health problems such as depression, PTSD, and other anxiety disorders can lead to physical illnesses among police (Freedy et

71

al., 2007; Zimmerman, 2010). Human systems designed to respond to stress include the central nervous system (CNS), hypothalamic-pituitary-adrenal (HPA) axis, and autonomic nervous system (ANS). Activation of these systems helps achieve stability after stressful events through "allostasis"—systems designed to promote adaptation from physiological changes brought about by stress (McEwen, 2017). Allostasis requires constant adjustment of autonomic function, behaviors, and hormones. However, chronic stress can disrupt allostasis that leads to wear and tear on the body and to psychological, metabolic, inflammatory, and cardiovascular disease (McEwen, 2017).

LIFE EXPECTANCY OF POLICE

Given exposure to high levels of stress and trauma and subsequent poor physical health, officers may die at an earlier age than workers in the general population. At present, there is limited research on the life expectancy of police officers. One often quoted study is that of Raub (1987) which compared Illinois State Police retirees to actuarial standard tables. Results suggested that police officers who retired during a 33-year period were more likely to be alive than other state employees. Another study, the CalPERS Experience Study (2010), reported that California police officers lived to be approximately the same age as other state employees after retirement. Violanti et al. (2014) found different results in a study that compared life expectancy and the probability of death of male police officers vs. the general U.S. male population. The study also examined years of potential life lost (YPLL) to police service between these two populations due to earlier than expected deaths.

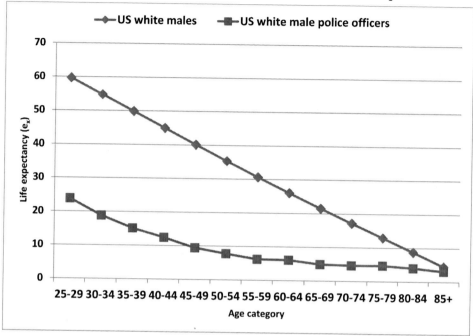

Figure 4.1
Life Expectancy of Police Compared to the General U.S. Population

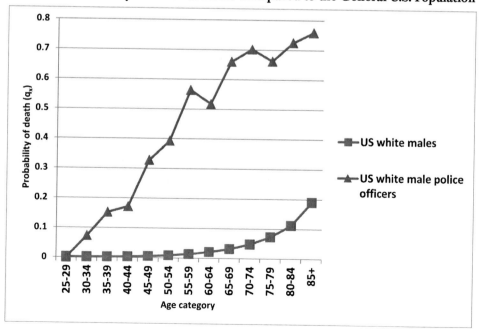

Figure 4.2
Statistical Probability of Death of Police Compared to the General U.S. Population

For each five-year age category, from 25–85 years of age, police officers had a lower life expectancy than the U.S. population (Figure 4.1). *The life expectancy of police officers was shorter and more pronounced for younger ages.* For example, an officer who lived to the beginning of age 50 during the period 1950–2005 was expected to live only 7.8 additional years while the estimate for U.S. white male for the same period was 35 years. On average, the life expectancy of white male police officers in our sample was significantly lower than the U.S. white male population (mean difference in life expectancy = 21.9 years). The statistical probability of death (Figure 4.2) was also higher among police across all age categories. For example, a police officer in the 50–54-year age category had close to a 40% probability of death vs. a male in the general population in the same age category having less than a 1% probability of death. Overall, male police officers had a significantly higher average probability of death than did males in the general population (mean difference in the probability of dying between police officers and the general population = 40%).

Years of Potential Life Lost

Police departments who are already short on personnel and facing decreased budgets can have a problem with officers who die earlier than they should due to heart attacks or other illnesses. Years of potential life lost (YPLL) is an estimate of the average years a person would have lived if they had not died prematurely (Gardner & Sanborn, 1990). YPLL was calculated by subtracting the actual age of death from a predetermined minimum age. YPLL was calculated based on an end point of the age of 75 years which was the average life expectancy in the United States the year this study was done (National Center for Health Statistics). In the Violanti et al. (2014) study, years of potential life lost was higher in all police age categories compared to the general population and clustered primarily in younger age groups. For example, the ratio of YPLL was over 38 times larger for police in the 40-44-year age group. Employing health and wellness programs will not only help officers feel and perform better and live longer but will also provide for a longer period of police service.

POLICE STRESS AND CARDIOVASCULAR DISEASE (CVD)

Persons who enter police work are generally part of a healthy work population but appear to deteriorate physically and psychologically as years of police service increase (Violanti, Vena, & Petralia, 1998). A 22-year prospective study of Helsinki police officers (Pyorala, Miettinen, Halonen, Laakso, & Pyorala, 2000) hypothesized that complex clustering of risk factors could be predictive of CVD and stroke risk. A cross-sectional study of metabolic syndrome in a sample of male police officers in Texas found that prevalence of CVD in male police officers was higher than the American male population, placing law enforcement officers at increased risk for future CVD morbidity and mortality (Humbarger, Crouse, Womack, & Green, 2004).

It is commonly asserted than stress is a factor in a higher risk for CVD. The police, under conditions of high stress, may therefore be more susceptible to CVD. A meta-analysis of workplace stressors and health outcomes showed that stressors, such as work-family conflict, job insecurity, high job demand, low job control, and lack of social support, were associated with poor physical and mental health (Goh et al., 2015). The study also showed that high job demands raised the odds of having a physician-diagnosed illness by 35%. Another study reported that job strain increased the likelihood of CVD by 23% (Kivim‰ki et al., 2012). Stress may play a major role in the development and maintenance of obesity in individuals that in turn can lead to CVD (Van der Valk, Savas, & van Rossum, 2018).

In a mortality cohort of police officers from 1950-2005, white male officers exhibited significantly higher than expected mortality from all diseases of the circulatory system and arteriosclerotic heart disease (Vena et al., 2014). The metabolic syndrome, a collection of three or more out of five cardiovascular risk components, has also been noted among police officers, with an estimated prevalence of 26.7% among urban police officers in the eastern United States (Hartley et al., 2012). Garbarino and Magnavita (2015) found that the most common components of metabolic syndrome in police constables were hypertriglyceridemia and low HDL cholesterol, and 22.7% police constables were hypertensive. Interestingly, the majority of fatal heart attacks in the present study occurred in the male 40–50 years age group. Feuer and Rosenman (1986) and Vena et al. (2014) found an inverse relationship between heart disease and age, indicating that male police officers most susceptible to heart disease were affected at younger ages.

Violanti, Fekedulegn, Shi and Andrew (2020), in a 22-year study of CVD among police deaths registered in the National Law Enforcement Officer Memorial Fund database, indicate that there was a significant upward trend in on-duty job-related illness deaths during this period (1997–2018) (β = 0.75, p-value <0.0001) (Figure 4.3). The Violanti et al. (2020) study showed that cardiovascular deaths that *occurred on duty* were the third leading cause of on-duty death among police officers in the United States. In total, there were 3,645 police deaths reported to NELOMF during the 22-year study period. Of those, 646 deaths were attributed to job-related illnesses; 94.7% of the deceased were men. Two-thirds (58.8%) of the deaths were described as being accidental (non-traffic) at work, while the remaining 41.2% occurred during a felony incident. Deceased officers ranged in age from 21–74 years, with the majority (74.3%) being in the 40-60 years age group. Sixty-three percent (67.5%) of the deceased officers served at least 15 years on the job. The largest percentage of the deaths was from the northeast (36%), followed by the South (30%), the Midwest (16%) and the West (9%), while 10% of the sample had missing information on regions.

Circulatory-related disease (52.6%) was the most common cause of death (Figure 4.3). The average age of on-duty death from CVD was 48 years of age. Among circulatory causes, 81.8% were due to a fatal heart attack, 2.1% from stroke, 2.1% from cardiac arrest and 14.2% probable circulatory causes (i.e. collapsed during training exercise, myocardial infarction, unresponsive after chest pains). Approximately 21% of deaths occurred during training situations (*n*=111), 85 of those resulting from cardiac incidents. The majority of cardiac-related deaths occurred at relatively younger ages (74.3% were in the 40–60-year age group). *The average age of on-duty death due to a heart attack was 46.5 years.* The majority of circulatory deaths occurred during and after atypical physical exertion or emotional strain described as:

- A physical struggle;
- Performing a search and rescue mission;
- Performing emergency medical treatment;
- Responding to a situation that involves a serious injury or death;
- A high speed response or pursuit on foot or in a vehicle;

Figure 4.3
Trend of Increasing On Duty Cardiovascular Deaths among Police. 1997–2018

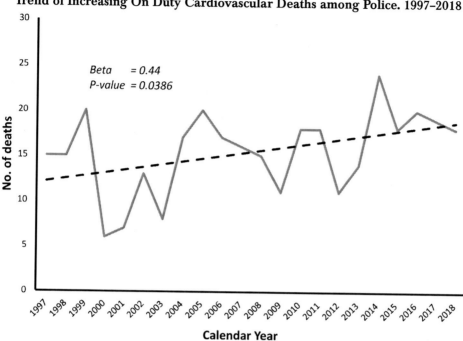

- Other health exposures (e.g. chemicals, hazardous materials);
- Training incidents. (Violanti, Fekedulegn, Shi and Andrew, 2020.)

The high rate of on-duty cardiac events may be a result of extremely stressful work events without warning coupled with the sedentary nature of police work (Zimmerman, 2012). This sort of strenuous and unexpected activity places increased demands on the cardiovascular system, especially for persons in poor physical condition (Mittleman et al., 1993). Varvargou et al. (2014) found that sudden cardiac death among police officers was considerably higher when they were involved in activities other than routine non-emergency duties. Examples were the pursuit of suspects, physical altercations, restraints and maintaining order in disaster situations. Lipovetzky et al. (2007) found that negative emotional experiences at work could trigger an acute coronary syndrome episode. Smyth et al. (2016) found that emotional upset are triggers associated with first acute myocardial infarction in men and women, and in all age groups, with no significant effect modifiers. Buckley et al. (2015) reported that episodes of intense anger and increased anxiety are associated with increased relative risk for acute coronary occlusion.

Stress and obesity are related (van der Valk & van Rossum, 2018), and obesity may add to health problems among police officers. A recent study suggested that overweight and obesity were more prevalent among law enforcement personnel than the general population (Ramey, Downing, & Franke, 2009), and lack of regular physical exercise is one of the occupational risk factors contributing to the higher prevalence of elevated blood pressure, metabolic syndrome, and CVD among emergency responders such as police officers (Kales, Tsismenakis, Zhang, & Soteriades, 2009). Police officers tend to report increased food consumption, a high-fat diet, and decreased physical activity in response to high levels of occupational stress (Grencik, 1973). The average BMI among male and female police officers in a recent police study was 29.2 and 26.1, respectively (Charles et al., 2007). These values are higher than those of adults over the age of 20 in the general U.S. population. In nine Midwestern states in the U.S., nearly 83% of police officers were overweight (BMI > 25) and similar findings were reported among retired police officers from Milwaukee (85% with a BMI > 25) (Ramey et al., 2009), which is much greater than the percentage of U.S. adults who are overweight or obese (66%). In another study, 9% of officers claimed they rarely exercised, 38% exercised 1–2 days a week, 32% exercised 3–4 days a week, and only 21% exercised 5 or more days a week (Richmond, Wodak, Kehoe, & Heather, 1998). These proportions are lower than the prevalence of regular physical activity (i.e. at least 30 minutes of moderate intensity physical activity most days of the week) among women (47%) and men (50%) in the general U.S. population (Kruger & Kohl, 2008).

In a recent study by Gu et al. (2016) the obesity rate was the second highest for police among 41 occupational categories, and the annual change in obesity prevalence was two times higher than for the U.S. population in the period from 1997–2002. A recent police cohort study revealed that the prevalence of obesity was 33.6% among North American police officers. Officers who may be in poor physical condition may be at higher risk for cardiac events when involved in activities involving mental strain (Ramey et al., 2009). The U.S. National Health Interview Survey data showed a higher prevalence of obesity (BMI $\geq$ 30 kg/m^2) both in non-Hispanic white men and women working in the protective service occupations compared to the general working population (Gu et al., 2016). Wright et al. (1995) compared male police officers' traditional cardiovascular risk factors with non-police male workers and found that police officers had a significantly higher BMI. In a statewide study on physical fitness in police officers, Violanti et al. (2016) found that officers who had higher levels of body fat were in poorer physical condition and did not perform as well on fitness tests as those with lower body fat.

POST-TRAUMATIC STRESS DISORDER (PTSD): EFFECTS ON POLICE HEALTH

A number of studies have focused on the general population and on police officers specifically, which indicate that individuals with PTSD are at an increased risk of CVD, coronary heart disease, hypertension, and stroke (Coughlin, 2011; Sareen et al., 2007; Violanti, Andrew et al., 2006; Violanti, Fekedulegn et al., 2006). PTSD symptoms have also been found to be associated with a reduction in blood flow, indicating poor artery health (Violanti, Fekedulegn et al., 2006). In a cross-sectional study of 2,970 general population participants, those with PTSD were found to be three times more likely to have type 2 diabetes compared to individuals without a traumatic event (Lukaschek et al., 2013). Gupta (2013) conducted a review of the literature and found that PTSD has been shown to be associated with a wide range of chronic diseases other than CVD and diabetes (Gupta, 2013). These include diseases such as chronic fatigue syndrome, fibromyalgia, gastrointestinal disorders, autoimmune disorders, and chronic pain syndromes such as migraine headaches (Gupta, 2013; Sareen et al., 2007). The frequency of experienced traumatic events has been found to correlate with symptom severity (Uddin et al., 2010). For this reason, officers who are exposed to multiple traumatic incidents may experience more severe symptoms compared to individuals who have had relatively few traumatic events.

A study by Violanti et al. (2006) examined associations between PTSD symptoms and metabolic syndrome in police officers. The metabolic syndrome is a cluster of components believed to be associated with CVD. The National Cholesterol Education Program (NCEP) Expert Panel on Detection, Evaluation, and Treatment of High Blood

Cholesterol in Adults (ATP III) (Expert Panel on Detection, Evaluation, and Treatment of High Blood Cholesterol in Adults, 1999) put forth guidelines for the proposed clinical definitions of the metabolic syndrome in adults to aid in diagnosis and recommended preventive interventions for this syndrome. Criteria for the metabolic syndrome include: (1) elevated waist circumference, >40″ in men, >35″ in women; (2) elevated triglycerides, >150 mg/dL; (3) reduced high density lipids (HDL) cholesterol, <40 mg/DL for men, <50 mg/dL for women; (4) glucose intolerance, fasting glucose >100 mg/DL; and (5) hypertension, systolic BP >130 mm Hg or diastolic BP >85 mm Hg. Three or more of these five components fulfill the requirement for metabolic syndrome. Results indicated a significantly increased prevalence of the metabolic syndrome among those officers in the severe PTSD symptom category compared with the lowest PTSD severity category were approximately *three times more likely* to have the metabolic syndrome (Violanti et al., 2006).

NEUROLOGICAL PROCESSES: TRAUMA EFFECTS ON THE BRAIN AND POLICE DECISION-MAKING

Police work routinely engages officers in rapid decision-making situations in which the inhibition of a response may result in potentially dangerous outcomes. PTSD symptoms are associated with a dysregulation of processes in the brain (Bremner, 2003; Liberzon & Martis, 2006) and such dysregulation can persist for years after the trauma (McFarlane, Weber, & Clark, 1993). Recent studies have demonstrated that PTSD symptoms have long-term effects on the structure and function of the brain (Bremner, 2003; Liberzon & Martis, 2006). Thus, relatively greater elevations of PTSD symptoms can effect differing function in the brain associated with trauma intrusion and avoidance symptoms.

Covey, Shucard, Violanti, Lee, and Shucard (2013) examined electro≠physiological brain measures of response processes using a visual "Go/No Go" letter recognition task. "Go/no go" refers to a reaction task for recognition of stimuli presented to the officer on a screen. The study required the officer to make rapid decisions whether to respond or not to certain letters. Results suggested that cognitive impairments from PTSD negatively compromise mechanisms associated with attention and decision making in police officers primarily in those officers who had higher PTSD symptoms. The study concluded that PTSD can lead to increased danger and poorer decision making in critical police incidents.

PTSD may not only affect neurological processes but also physical brain structure as well. Shucard et al. (2012) found that chronic re-experiencing of traumatic events was significantly related to affective ratings of negative (trauma related) picture stimuli to brain structures involved in the processing of fear. In this study, police officers with exposure to trauma-related stressors underwent structural magnetic resonance imaging (MRI). They were also exposed to arousal ratings of neutral and negative (trauma-related) picture stimuli. Relationships were examined among PTSD symptom scores (avoidance, re-experiencing, and hyperarousal), picture ratings, structural MRI measures, and number of trauma exposures. The greater the number of times that officers were exposed to traumatic events, the greater the likelihood that they would have increased PTSD symptomatology and increased brain atrophy.

POLICE BURNOUT AND HEALTH

Burnout results from chronic stress in the workplace. It is characterized by depersonalization, reduced professional efficacy, and exhaustion (Maslach & Jackson, 1981). In a study conducted in Israeli police officers, the mean burnout score was found to be higher than the national average (3.05 vs 2.8) (Malach-Pines & Keinan, 2007). In police, burnout is associated with organizational and operational stress including lack of support from the community or the lack of promotion. Exhaustion and depersonalization positively correlated to a number of psychological and somatic symptoms (Talavera-Velasco et al., 2018). Reduced professional efficacy was negatively correlated to factors such as anxiety, insomnia, severe depression, and somatic symptoms. Police perception of danger and unfairness were also associated with burnout (McCarty & Slokan, 2012). Detrimental consequences of burnout can include substance abuse, decreased quality of service, and impaired mental and physical health.

Burnout has been associated with negative effects on biological stress hormones which can lead to an imbalance of protective systems in the body. Cortisol is a primary stress hormone which is secreted during the stress response. This hormone is necessary for the proper functioning of many bodily systems designed to maintain balanced hormonal factors. Chronic stress may result in depleted cortisol and failure in normal daily patterns of cortisol secretion (Hannibal & Bishop, 2014). A study by McCanlies et al. (2014) found that higher burnout symptoms in police officers resulted in dysregulated waking cortisol pattern and a lower diurnal cortisol production. McCanlies et al. (2014) concluded that cynicism and exhaustion may be associated with diminished cortisol secretion and increased risk for disease in police officers. Fernandez-Sanchez et al. (2018) found that stress was associated with burnout in female nurses and that average cortisol secretion was lower in nurses without burnout compared to nurses with high scores on at least one burnout subscale (Fernandez-Sanchez et al., 2018). Similarly, Wingenfeld et al. (2009) found that people with at least two burnout components had higher levels of cortisol compared to individuals with either one or no burnout components (Wingenfeld et al., 2009). It has been suggested that exhaustion is a primary component of burnout (Jonsdottir et al., 2019).

STRESS AND DNA EFFECTS

Psychological stress can increase the rate of cell aging through different pathways (Epel et al., 2004). Telomere attrition, which accelerates aging and susceptibility to disease, is one DNA factor affected by stress (Révész et al., 2015). Telomere attrition has been described as a precursor of premature morbidity and mortality related to exposure to chronic stress (Lu et al., 2019). Telomeres are repetitive DNA sequences that, in concert with telomere binding proteins, cap the ends of chromosomes and protect cellular replication (Blackburn, 2005). Maintenance of telomere length depends, in part, on the activity of the enzyme (Smogorzewska & de Lange, 2004). Telomere length is considered to be related to cell viability because when telomeres shorten to a certain length it may result in cell death. Telomere length is highly variable at birth, with dramatic decreases in the neonatal and early childhood period, and slower attrition rates in adulthood (Baird & Kipling, 2004). Thus, telomere length attrition is likely to be a product of multiple influences on telomere maintenance, tissue composition and differences in telomere attrition rates, reflecting the cumulative burden of stress-related physiological changes such as inflammation and immune senescence.

To date, trauma, recent stressful life events, shift work, overtime and long work hours, and other operationally relevant variables have been associated with telomere length attrition and/or low telomerase activity (Verhoeven et al., 2015; Stein et al., 2018). In a recent review, Rentscher et al. (2020) stated that the most consistent findings of the effects of work-related stressors on biological aging are the effects of work schedules. Stein et al. (2018) found that lack of perceived social support may be associated with biological aging in persons who have endured extreme stress during early adulthood. One promising finding by Chmelar et al. (2017) suggests that having a supportive work environment and work-related health moderates the relationship between aging and telomere length.

SHIFT WORK, STRESS, AND HEALTH

Police officers report that shift work is one of the most stressful functions of their job (Vila & Kenney, 2002; Charles et al., 2007). Previous studies have suggested that shift work is associated with health outcomes such as cardiovascular disease. Shift work imposes a rearrangement of awake and sleep time which leads to a disruption of circadian rhythm and an internal de-synchronization and subsequent psychological and physiological disturbances (Vila & Kenney, 2002).

Shift work and sleep loss are major sources of fatigue for police officers. Recent cross-sectional research has also shown that shift work and long work hours increase absenteeism in policing (Fekedulegn et al., 2014). Biological factors that lead to depression have been associated with shift work. The reduction of melatonin production, increased stress, and increased inflammation have been found to be associated with depression (Monteleone, Marttiadis & Maj, 2011). Altered circadian rhythms in melatonin secretions have been found among those suffering from depression. Killgore et al. (2007) suggested that sleep deprivation impairs the ability to integrate emotion and cognition to guide moral judgment. Sleep-deprived participants showed significantly greater difficulty, emotionally, in judging decisions as appropriate relative to inappropriate. These findings suggest that sleep deprivation has a debilitating effect on judgment and decision-making processes. In another study on judgment and sleep deprivation (Killgore, Balkin, & Wesenten, 2005) individuals tended to make risky decisions. These findings suggest that cognitive functions related to decision making may be particularly vulnerable to sleep loss (Rouch, Wild, Ansiau, & Marquie, 2005).

A study by Violanti et al. (2009) indicated a higher prevalence for depression in officers (12.5% for women and 6.2% for men officers) compared to the general population—data from the National Institute of Mental Health (NIMH) reported 5.2% prevalence for depression (Weissman et al., 1996). There were different levels of depressive symptoms on night shifts. Higher depression in male officers on the midnight shift may have been accounted for in part by a stronger need of officers to be part of the social cohesiveness associated with peers in the police organization (Paton et al., 2000). Working midnight shifts may lead to an isolation from the main thrust of male peer interaction and perpetuate feelings of disconnection from the group. This can prove stressful and exacerbate existing depressive states. Given the danger that officers face on a daily basis, such isolation can be meaningful in the sense that it negates the beneficial aspects of group social support. In addition, PTSD interacted significantly with afternoon shift. Male officers with higher PTSD symptomatology who worked afternoon shifts may be further placed at risk for additional exposure to traumatic work events. Afternoon shifts are generally the busiest in terms of crime, traffic, and answering citizen complaints. Such exposure may only worsen PTSD symptoms.

SHIFT WORK, STRESS, AND CANCER

Cancer is one of the most common diseases associated with shift work. Abnormal DNA methylation (methylation helps to regulate DNA) is an established early event in cancer and likely other human diseases, and it has been more prevalent in shift workers. Abnormal DNA methylation may underlie stress-related disease susceptibility related to shift work (Rashid, Shen, Morris, Issa, & Hamilton, 2001). Sleep loss, which is perhaps the most common complaint among shift workers, also alters DNA methylation patterns (Gaine, Chatterjee, & Abel, 2018). A study of Buffalo police officers found an increased risk of digestive cancer and cancer of the lymphatic and blood-forming tissues in officers with 10-19 years of service. Officers with this length of service had been previously identified to have the highest stress scores among Buffalo police officers. At the time of the cancer mortality study, Buffalo police officers also worked a difficult schedule requiring two of the three shifts to work 16 hours within a 24-hour period or "doubling back" (Vena, Violanti, & Petralia, 1998). Various cancers were represented in a 40-year mortality study of male police off?cers in Buffalo. By years of police service, higher than expected rates were observed for all malignant cancers with 1-9 years of service, for bladder cancer and leukemia with 10-19 years of service, and colon cancer with over 30 years of service (Violanti, Vena, & Petralia, 1998).

Studies suggest that stress may affect cancer risk at certain sites and populations (Wirth et al., 2013). The risk of cancers of the lymphatic and hematopoietic tissues seen in police mortality studies (Vena et al., 2014) in this study is interesting because other research has shown that leukemia and lymphoma can be caused by substantial psychological stress (Greene, 1966; Janerich et al., 1981). The increased risk for mortality of cancer of the colon could be due to a combination of risk factors, including lack of physical exercise and the somewhat sedentary physical activities of police work (Vena et al., 1985), job stress (Spiegelman & Wegman, 1985), irregular dietary habits (Violanti, 1985), and shift work that could affect the digestive cycle (IARC, 2010).

Immune system dysregulation due to shiftwork or sleep disruption may foster tumor development (Grandner & Drummond, 2007). Either long (8 hour) or short (6 hour) duration sleep has been associated with increased breast cancer risks in several large cohort studies. Shift work has been linked with increased risks for prostate, breast, and colorectal cancer, as well as non-Hodgkin's lymphoma, and the International Agency for Research on Cancer concluded that shift work is a probable human carcinogen (Errin et al., 2019). Several recent studies that were published after the review support and extend these observations (Hansen & Stevens, 2012; Knutsson et al., 2013).

Violanti, Fekedulgen, Shi and Andrew (2020) found that cancer deaths among police had increased from 1997–2018 (Figure 4.4). The majority of most recent cancer deaths were among officers involved with rescue and recovery during and after the 9/11 terrorist attack, suggesting possible exposure to potentially harmful chemicals, carcinogens, or hazardous substances as the risk factor. This included the World Trade Center, Pentagon, and Shanksville, Pennsylvania locations. The majority of deaths from cancer were due to lung cancer and associated lung diseases. The potential for law enforcement exposure to hazardous materials in the United States is high. This is evidenced by several police mortality studies, which show an increased risk for cancers associated with chemical exposures (Vena et al., 2014, Feur & Rosenman, 1986; Pyorala, et al., 2000). Officers are often called upon to investigate traffic accidents involving hazardous materials, or handle disaster situations where chemicals are released in the air. More than 60,000 chemicals are produced annually in the United States, of which the US Department of Transportation considers approximately 2000 are hazardous (https://www.federalregister.gov/documents/2020/05/11/2020-06205/hazardous-materials-harmonization-with-international-standards).

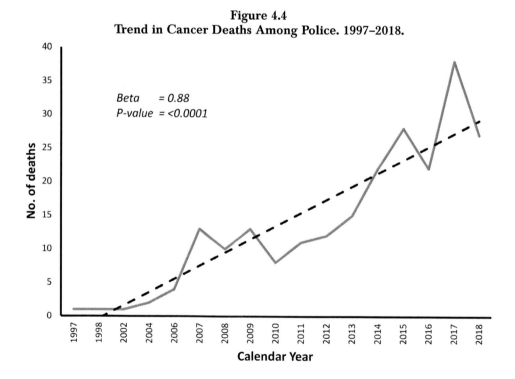

Figure 4.4
Trend in Cancer Deaths Among Police. 1997–2018.

This chapter has presented research and conjecture on the association between police stressors and physiological outcomes of disease. As we continue to examine the mental health of police officers, there is good evidence that stress will have not only an immediate but also a long-term effect on police physical health. The majority of officers tend to stay in policing for their entire career—generally a period of 20–25 years. Such a continued and intensified exposure over this lengthy period of time will highly likely exacerbate health problems among those who serve in this profession. Exposure and job socialization have a profound impact on police officers, and future research should include etiologic studies that can evaluate potential occupational factors that lead to increased risks. In the next chapter, we move to positive psychology and efforts to deal with stress and trauma. Resiliency, or the ability to bounce back from adversity, can have a protective effect against stress.

REFERENCES

Baird, D. M., & Kipling, D. (2004). The extent and significant of telomere loss with age. *Annals of the New York Academy of Science, 1019*(1), 265–268.

Blackburn, E. H. (2005). Telomeres and telomerase: Their mechanisms of action and the effects of altering their functions. *Federation of European Biochemical Societies Letters, 579*(4), 859–862.

Bremner, J. D. (2005). Effects of traumatic stress on brain structure and function: Relevance to early responses to trauma. *Journal of Trauma & Dissociation, 6*(2), 51–68.

Buckley, T., Hoo, S. Y., Fethney, J., Shaw, E., Hanson, P. S., & Tofler, G. H. (2015). Triggering of acute coronary occlusion by episodes of anger. *European Heart Journal: Acute Cardiovascular Care, 4*(6), 493–498. https://doi.org/10.1177/204887 2615568969

Burch, J. B., Tom, J., Zhai, Y., Criswell, L., Leo, E., & Ogoussan, K. (2009). Shiftwork impacts and adaptation among health care workers. *Occupational Medicine, 59,* 159–166.

CalPERS. (2010). California employees' retirement system experience study. Cardiovascular disease risk and morbidity among aging law enforcement officers. Actuarial Office; Los Angeles, CA.

Centers for Disease Control. Health and Economic Costs of Chronic Diseases. https://www.cdc.gov/chronicdisease/about/costs/index.htm Accessed 3-10-21.

Charles, L. E., Burchfiel, C. M., Fekedulegn, D., Vila, B., Hartley, T. A., Slaven J., . . . Mnatsakanova, A. (2007). Shift work and sleep: The Buffalo Police health study. *Policing: An International Journal of Police Strategies and Management, 30,* 215–227.

Chmelar, C., J'rres, R. A., Kronseder, A., M̧ller, A., Nowak, D., & Weigl, M. (2017). Associations between age, psychosocial work conditions, occupational well-being, and telomere length in geriatric care professionals: A mixed-methods study. *Journal of Occupational and Environmental Medicine, 59*(10), 949–955.

Coughlin, S. S. (2011). Post-traumatic stress disorder and cardiovascular disease. *The Open Cardiovascular Medicine Journal, 5,* 164–170.

Covey, T. J., Shucard, J. L., Violanti, J. M., Lee, J., & Shucard, D. W. (2013). The effects of exposure to traumatic stressors on inhibitory control in police officers: A dense electrode array study using a Go/NoGo continuous performance task. *International Journal of Psychophysiology, 87*(3), 363–375. https://doi.org/10.1016/j.ijpsycho.2013.03.009

Epel, E. S., Blackburn, E. H., Lin, J., Dhabhar, F. S., Adler, N. E., Morrow, J. D., & Cawthon, R. M. (2004). Accelerated telomere shortening in response to life stress. *Proceedings of the National Academy of Sciences, 101*(49), 17312–17315.

Erren, T. C., Morfeld, P., Grofl, J.V., Wild, U. & Lewis, P. (2019). "Night shift work" is probably carcinogenic: What about disturbed chronobiology in all walks of life? *Journal of Occupational Medical Toxicology, 14,* 29. https://doi.org/10.1186/s12995-019-0249-6

Expert Panel on Detection, Evaluation, and Treatment of High Blood Cholesterol in Adults. (2001). Executive Summary of the Third Report of the National Cholesterol Education Program (NCEP) Expert Panel on Detection, Evaluation, and Treatment of High Blood Cholesterol in Adults (Adult Treatment Panel III). *JAMA, 285*(19), 2486–2497. https://doi.org/10.1001/jama.285.19.2486

Fekedulegn, D., Burchfiel, C. M., Hartley, T. A., Baughman, P., Charles, L. E., Andrew, M. E., & Violanti, J. M. (2014). Work hours and absenteeism among police officers. *International Journal of Mental Health and Human Resilience, 15,* 267–276.

Fernández-Sánchez, J., Pérez-Mármol, J., Blásquez, A., Santos-Ruiz, A., & Peralta-Ram'rez, M. (2017). Association between burnout and cortisol secretion, perceived stress, and psychopathology in palliative care unit health professionals. *Palliative and Supportive Care, 16,* 1–12. 10.1017/S1478951517000244

Franke, W. D., Ramey, S. L., & Shelley, M. C. (2002). Relationship between cardiovascular disease morbidity, risk factors, and stress in a law enforcement cohort. *Journal of Occupational and Environmental Medicine, 44*(12), 1182–1189.

Freedy, J. R., Steenkamp, M. M., Magruder, K. M., Yeager, D. E., Zoller, J. S., Hueston, W. J., & Carek, P. J. (2010). Post-traumatic stress disorder screening test performance in civilian primary care. *Family Practice, 27*(6), 615–624. https://doi.org/10.1093/fampra/cmq049

Gaine, M. E., Chatterjee, S., & Abel, T. (2018). Sleep deprivation and the epigenome. *Frontiers in Neural Circuits, 12,* 14. https://doi.org/10.3389/fncir.2018.00014

Gardner, J. W., & Sanborn, J. S. (1990). Years of potential life lost (YPLL)—what does it measure? *Epidemiology (Cambridge, Mass.), 1*(4), 322–329. https://doi.org/10.1097/00001648-199007000-00012

Goh, J., Pfeffer, J., & Zenios, S. (2015). The relationship between workplace stressors and mortality and health costs in the United States. *Management Science, 62*(2), 608–628. 150313065100000. 10.1287/mnsc.2014.2115

Grencik, L. (1973). *The physical fitness of deputies assigned to the patrol function and its relationship to the formulation of entrance standards.* Washington, DC: U.S. Department of Justice, Law Enforcement Assistance Administration; U.S. Government Printing Office.

Gu, J. K., Charles, L. E., Andrew, M. E., Ma, C. C., Harley, T. A., Violanti, J. M., & Burchfiel, C. M. (2016). Prevalence of work-site injuries and relationship between obesity and injury among U.S. workers; NHIS 2004–2012. *Journal of Safety Research, 58,* 21–20. doi:10.1016/j.jsr.2016.06.001

Gupta, M. A. (2013). Review of somatic symptoms in post-traumatic stress disorder. *International Review of Psychiatry, 25,* 86–99.

Hannibal, K. E., & Bishop, M. D. (2014). Chronic stress, cortisol dysfunction, and pain: A psychoneuroendocrine rationale for stress management in pain rehabilitation. *Physical Therapy, 94*(12), 1816–1825. https://doi.org/10.2522/ptj .20130597

Hansen, J., & Stevens, R. G. (2012). Case-control study of shift-work and breast cancer risk in Danish nurses: Impact of shift systems. *European Journal of Cancer, 48*(11), 1722–1729. https://doi.org/10.1016/j.ejca.2011.07.005

Hazardous Materials: Harmonization with International Standards. https://www .federalregister.gov/documents/2020/05/11/2020-06205/hazardous-materials -harmonization-with-international-standards. Accessed 3-30-21.

Hemio, K., Puttonen, S., Viitasalo, K., Harma, M., Peltonen, M., & Lindstrom, J. (2015). Food and nutrient intake among workers with different shift systems. *Occupational and Environmental Medicine, 72*(7), 513–520. doi: 10.1136/oemed -2014-102624

Humbarger, C. D., Crouse, S. F., Womack, J. W., & Green, J. S. (2004). Frequency of metabolic syndrome in police officers compared to NCEP III prevalence values. *Medicine & Science in Sports & Exercise, 36*(5), S161. PubMed PMID: 00005768-200405001-00767

Jonsdottir, I. H., & Sjˆrs Dahlman, A. (2019). Mechanisms in endocrinology: Endocrine and immunological aspects of burnout: A narrative review. *European Journal of Endocrinology, 180*(3), R147–R158. https://doi.org/10.1530/EJE-18-0741

Kales, S. N., Tsismenakis, A. J., Zhang, C., & Soteriades, E. S. (2009). Blood pressure in firefighters, police officers, and other emergency responders. *American Journal of Hypertension, 22,* 11–20.

Killgore, W. D., Balkin, T. J., & Wesenten, N. J. (2005). Impaired decision making following 49 hours of sleep deprivation. *Journal of Sleep Research, 14,* 1–7.

Killgore, W. D., Killgore, D. B., Day, L. M., Li, C., Kamimori, G. H., & Balkin, T. J. (2007). The effects of 53 hours of sleep deprivation on moral judgment. *Sleep, 30,* 345–352.

Kivimaki, M., Nyberg, S. T., Batty, G. D., Fransson, E. I., Heikkila, K., Alfredsson, L., . . . Bjorner, J. B. (2012). Job strain as a risk factor for coronary heart disease: A collaborative meta-analysis of individual participant data. *Lancet (London, England), 380*(9852), 1491–1497. https://doi.org/10.1016/S0140-6736(12)60994-5

Knutsson, A., Alfredsson, L., Karlsson, B., Akerstedt, T., Fransson, E. et al. (2013). Breast cancer among shift workers: Results of the WOLF longitudinal cohort study. *Scandinavian Journal of Work, Environment and Health, 39*(2), 170–177. URL: http://dx.doi.org/10.5271/sjweh.3323

Liberzon, I., & Martis, B. (2006). Neuroimaging studies of emotional responses in PTSD. *The Sciences, 1071,* 87–109.

Lipovetzky, N., Hod, H., Roth, A., Kishon, Y., Sclarovsky, S., & Green, M. S. (2007). Emotional events and anger at the workplace as triggers for a first event of the acute coronary syndrome: A case-crossover study. *The Israel Medical Association Journal, 9*(4), 310–315.

Lu, D., Palmer, J. R., Rosenberg, L., Shields, A. E., Orr, E. H., DeVivo, I., & Cozier, Y. C. (2019). Perceived racism in relation to telomere length among African American women in the Black Women's Health Study. *Annals of Epidemiology, 36,* 33–39.

Lukaschek, K., Baumert, J., Kruse, J., Emeny, R. T., Lacruz, M. E., Huth, C., . . . KORA Investigators. (2013). Relationship between posttraumatic stress disorder and type 2 diabetes in a population-based cross-sectional study with 2,970 participants. *Journal of Psychosomatic Research, 74,* 340–345. https://doi.org/10.1016/j.jpsychores.2012.12.011

Malach-Pines, A., & Keinan, G. (2007). Stress and burnout in Israeli police officers during a Palestinian uprising (Intifada). *International Journal of Stress Management, 14*(2), 160–174. https://doi.org/10.1037/1072-5245.14.2.160

Maslach, C., & Jackson, S. E. (1981). The measurement of experienced burnout. *Journal of Occupational Behavior, 2,* 99–113. doi: 10.1002/job.4030020205

McCanlies, E. C., Mnatsakanova, A., Andrew, M. E., Burchfiel, C. M., & Violanti, J. M. (2014). Positive psychological factors are associated with lower PTSD symptoms among police officers: post Hurricane Katrina. *Stress and Health, 30*(5), 405–415. doi: 10.1002/smi.2615

McCarty, W. P., & Skogan, W. G. (2013). Job-related burnout among civilian and sworn police personnel. *Police Quarterly, 16*(1), 66–84. https://doi.org/10.1177/1098611112457357

McEwen, B. S. (2017). Allostasis and the epigenetics of brain and body health over the life course: The brain on stress. *JAMA psychiatry, 74*(6), 551–552. https://doi.org/10.1001/jamapsychiatry.2017.0270.

McFarlane, A. C., Weber, D. L., & Clark, C. R. (1993). Abnormal stimulus processing in posttraumatic stress disorder. *Biological Psychiatry, 34,* 311–320.

Mittleman, M. A., Maclure, M., Tofler, G. H., Sherwood, J. B., Goldberg, R. J., & Muller, J. E. (1993). Triggering of acute myocardial infarction by heavy physical exertion. Protection against triggering by regular exertion. Determinants of Myocardial Infarction Onset Study Investigators. *The New England Journal of Medicine, 329*(23), 1677–1683. https://doi.org/10.1056/NEJM199312023292301

Monteleone, P., Martiadis, V., & Maj, M. (2011). Circadian rhythms and treatment implications in depression. *Progress in Neuro-Psychopharmacological & Biological Psychiatry, 35*(7), 1569–1574. doi:S0278-5846(10)00294-0 [pii] 10.1016/j.pnpbp .2010.07.028

Nagaraja, A. S., Sadaoui, N. C., Dorniak, P. L., Lutgendorf, S. K., & Sood, A. K. (2016). SnapShot: Stress and disease. *Cell Metabolism, 23*(2), 388–388.e1. https: //doi.org/10.1016/j.cmet.2016.01.015

National Center for Health Statistics. *Life expectancy.* https://www.cdc.gov/nchs /fastats/life-expectancy.htm

Ortho-Gomer, K. (1983). Intervention on coronary risk factors by adapting a shift work schedule to biologic rhythmicity. *Psychosomatic Medicine, 45*(5), 407–415.

Pyorala, M., Miettinen, H., Halonen, P., Laakso, M., & Pyorala K. (2000). Insulin resistance syndrome predicts the risk of coronary heart disease and stroke in healthy middle-aged men: The 22-year follow-up results of the Helsinki Policemen Study. *Arteriosclerotic Thrombosis and Vascular Biology, 20*(2), 538–544.

Ramey, S. L, Franke, W. D., & Shelley, M. C. (2004). Relationship among risk factors for nephrolithiasis, cardiovascular disease, and ethnicity: Focus on a law enforcement cohort. *AAOHN Journal, 52,* 116–121.

Rashid, A., Shen, L., Morris, J. S., Issa, J. P., & Hamilton, S. R. (2001). CpG island methylation in colorectal adenomas. *The American Journal of Pathology, 159*(3), 1129–1135. https://doi.org/10.1016/S0002-9440(10)61789-0

Raub, R. A. (1987). *Police officer retirement: The beginning of a long life.* National Institute of Justice/National Criminal Justice Reference Service; Rockville, MD: 1987. article 109485.

Rentscher, K. E., Carroll, J. E., & Mitchell, C. (2020). Psychosocial stressors and telomere length: A current review of the science. *Annual Review of Public Health, 41,* 223–245.

Révész, D., Milaneschi Y., Verhoeven, J. E., Lin J., & Pinninx, B. W. J. H. (2015). Longitudinal associations between metabolic syndrome components and telomere shortening. *The Journal of Clinical Endocrinology & Metabolism, 100*(8), 3050–3059.

Richmond, R. L., Wodak, A., Kehoe, L., & Heather, N. (1998). How healthy are the police? A survey of life-style factors. *Addiction, 93,* 1729–1737.

Rouch, I., Wild, P., Ansiau, D., & Marquié, J-C. (2005). Shiftwork experience, age and cognitive performance. *Ergonomics, 48,* 1282–1293.

Sareen, J., Cox, B. J., Stein, M. B., Afifi, T. O., Fleet, C., & Asmundson, G. J. (2007). Physical and mental comorbidity, disability, and suicidal behavior associated with posttraumatic stress disorder in a large community sample. *Psychosomatic Medicine, 69,* 242–248.

Shucard, J. L., Cox, J., Shucard, D. W., Fetter, H., Chung, C., Ramasamy, D., & Violanti, J. M. (2012). Symptoms of posttraumatic stress disorder and exposure to traumatic stressors are related to brain structural volumes and behavioral measures of affective stimulus processing in police officers. *Psychiatry Research, 204*(1), 25–31. https://doi.org/10.1016/j.pscychresns.2012.04.006

Smith, J. E., Jr., & Tooker, G. G. (2021). Health and fitness in law enforcement: A voluntary model program response to a critical issue. Retrieved March 10, 2021, from CALEA website: http://www.calea.org/Online/newsletter/No87/healthfitness.htm

Smogorzewska, A., & de Lange, T. (2004). Regulation of telomerase by telomeric proteins. *Annual Review of Biochemistry, 73,* 177–208.

Stein, J. Y., Levin, Y., Lahav, Y., Uziel O., Abumock, H., & Solomon, Z. (2018). Perceived social support, loneliness, and later life telomere length following wartime captivity. *Health Psychology, 37*(11), 1067–1076.

Smyth, A., O'Donnell, M., Lamelas, P., Teo, K., Rangarajan, S. & Yusuf, S. and On behalf of the INTERHEART Investigators. (2016). Physical activity and anger or emotional upset as triggers of acute myocardial infarction. *Circulation, 134,* 1059–1067.

Suicide contagion and the reporting of suicide: Recommendations from a national workshop. https://www.sprc.org/resources-programs/suicide-contagion-reporting-suicide-recommendations-national-workshop. Accessed 3-29-21

Talavera-Velasco, B., Luceño-Moreno, L., Martín-García, J., & Garceiía-Albuerne, Y. (2018). Psychosocial risk factors, burnout and hardy personality as variables associated with mental health in police officers. *Frontiers in Psychology, 9,* 1478. https://doi.org/10.3389/fpsyg.2018.01478

Uddin, M., Aiello, A. E., Wildman, D. E., Koenen, K. C., Pawelec, G., de Los Santos, R., . . . Galea, S. (2010). Epigenetic and immune function profiles associated with posttraumatic stress disorder. *Proceedings of the National Academy of Sciences U.S., 107,* 9470–9475.

van der Valk, E. S., Savas, M., & van Rossum, E. (2018). Stress and obesity: Are there more susceptible individuals? *Current Obesity Reports, 7*(2), 193–203. https://doi.org/10.1007/s13679-018-0306-y

Varvarigou, V., Farioli, A., Korre, M., Sato, S., Dahabreh, I. J., & Kales, S. N. (2014). Law enforcement duties and sudden cardiac death among police officers in United States: Case distribution study. *BMJ (Clinical research ed.), 349,* g6534. https://doi.org/10.1136/bmj.g6534

Vena, J. E., Charles, L. E., Gu, J. K., Burchfiel, C. M., Andrew, M. E., Fekedulegn, D., & Violanti, J. M. (2014). Mortality of a police cohort: 1950–2005. *Journal of Law Enforcement Leadership and Ethics, 1*(1) 7–30.

Verhoeven, J. E., van Oppen, P., Puterman, E., Elzinga, B., & Penninx, B. W. (2015). The association of early and recent psychosocial life stress with leukocyte telomere length. *Psychosomatic Medicine, 77*(8), 882–891.

Vila, B., & Kenney, D. J. (2002). Tired cops: The prevalence and potential consequences of police fatigue. *NIJ Journal,* no. 248, 2002. https://www.ojp.gov/pdf files1/jr000248d.pdf

Violanti, J. M., Vena, J. E., & Petralia, S. (1998). Mortality of a police cohort: 1950–1990. *American Journal of Industrial Medicine, 33*(4), 366–373. https://doi.org/10.1002/(sici)1097-0274(199804)33:4<366::aid-ajim6>3.0.co;2-s

Violanti, J. M., Fekedulegn, D., Hartley, T. A., Andrew, M. E., Charles, L. E., Mnatsakanova, A., & Burchfiel, C. M. (2006). Police trauma and cardiovascular dis- ease: Association between PTSD symptoms and metabolic syndrome. *International Journal of Emergency Mental Health, 8,* 227–237.

Violanti, J. M., Andrew, M. E., Burchfiel, C. M., Dorn, J., Hartley, T. A., & Miller, D. B. (2006). Posttraumatic stress syndrome symptoms and subclinical cardiovascular disease in police officers. *International Journal of Stress Management, 13,* 541–554.

Violanti, J. M., Andrew, M., Burchfiel, C. M., Hartley, T. A., Charles, L. E., & Miller, D. B. (2007). Post-traumatic stress symptoms and cortisol patterns among police officers. *Policing–An International Journal of Police Strategies & Management, 30,* 189–202.

Violanti, J. M., Slaven, J. E., Charles, L. E., Mnatsakanova, A., Andrew, M. E., Hartley, T. A., & Burchfiel, C. M. (2009). A prospective study of shift work and depression in police officers. *American Journal of Epidemiology, 169*(S11), S124.

Violanti, J. M., Burchfiel, C. M., Hartley, T. A., Mnatsakanova, A., Fekedulegn, D., Andrew, M. E, . . . Charles, L. E. (2009). Atypical work hours and metabolic syndrome among police officers. *Archives of Environmental and Occupational Health, 64,* 194–201.

Violanti, J. M., Fekedulegn, D., Hartley, T. A., Andrew, M. E., Gu, J. K., & Burchfiel, C. M. (2013). Life expectancy in police officers: A comparison with the U.S. general population. *International Journal of Emergency Mental Health, 15*(4), 217–228.

Violanti, J. M., Fekedulegn, D., Andrew, M. E., Charles, L. E., Hartley, T. A., Vila, B., & Burchfiel, C. M. (2013). Shift work and long term injury among police officers. *Scandinavian Journal of Work and Environmental Health, 39,* 361–368.

Violanti, J. M., Fekedulegn, D., Hartley, T. A., Andrew, M. E., Gu, J. K., & Burchfiel, C. M. (2013). Life expectancy in police officers: A comparison with the U.S. general population. *International Journal of Emergency Mental Health, 15*(4), 217–228.

Violanti, J. M., Ma, C. C., Fekedulegn, D., Andrew, M. E., Gu, J. K., Hartley, T. A., . . . Burchfiel, C. M. (2016). Association between body fat percentage and fitness among police officers: A statewide study. *Safety and Health at Work, 8,* 36–41. PMC 5355530

Violanti, J. M., Fekedulegn, D., Shi, M., & Andrew, M. E. (2020). Hidden danger: A 22-year analysis of law enforcement deaths associated with duty related illnesses (1997-2018). *Policing: An International Journal of Police Strategies & Management, 43*(2), 330–344.

Weissman, M. M., Bland, R. C., Canino, G. J., & Faravelli, C. (1996). Cross-national epidemiology of major depression and bipolar disorder. *JAMA, 276,* 293–299.

Wingenfeld, K., Schulz, M., Damkroeger, A., Rose, M., & Driessen, M. (2009). Elevated diurnal salivary cortisol in nurses is associated with burnout but not with vital exhaustion. *Psychoneuroendocrinology, 34*(8), 1144–1151. https://doi.org /10.1016/j.psyneuen.2009.02.015

Zimmerman, F. H. (2012). Cardiovascular disease and risk factors in law enforcement personnel: A comprehensive review. *Cardiology in Review, 20*(4), 159–166.

Chapter 5

RESILIENCE: DE-STRESSING STRESS

Resilience is accepting your new reality, even if it's less good than the one you had before. You can fight it, you can do nothing but scream about what you've lost, or you can accept that and try to put together something that's good.

—Elizabeth Edwards

Resilience has been simply defined as bouncing back from adversity. There are, however, many dimensions of resiliency. It has long been believed that exposure to trauma inevitably leads to pathologies such as PTSD and depression. Recent research in the area of positive psychology has opened the realization that these pathologies do not occur in all people. The question is why some people do not suffer from PTSD or depression or other mental difficulties while others do. In police work, where high stress events and exposure to potentially traumatic events is common, resilience and recovery is essential. This chapter provides an overview of factors related to resilience and examines some of the mechanisms that underpin resilience in police work. Additionally, suggestions are made that may help police organizations foster resiliency in officers. It is important that the protective aspect of resilience against stress be explained and employed in the profession of policing.

WHAT IS RESILIENCE?

- Resilience has been defined as "the process of adapting well in the face of adversity, trauma, tragedy, threats or even significant sources of threat" (American Psychological Association, 2014, para. 4);

- A stable trajectory of healthy functioning after a highly adverse event;
- Capacity of a dynamic system to adapt successfully to disturbances;
- The process to harness resources to sustain well-being and reintegration of self;
- The process of adapting to and bouncing back from adversity experience (Southwick, Bonanno, Masten, Panter-Brick & Yehuda, 2014).

Paton, Violanti, and Smith (2003) defined resilience as the capacity of individuals, communities and organizations, and the systems that facilitate their performance, to maintain relationships and balance between elements in the presence of significant disturbances as a result of a capability to draw upon their resources and competencies to manage the demands, challenges and changes encountered. Resilience has also been defined as "ordinary magic" (Masten, 2001). Findings from various studies on children have found that resilience has to do with how well people adapt to adversity. Masten (2001) has called this the ordinary magic of resiliency, meaning that resilience is made of ordinary rather than extraordinary processes. According to Masten (2001) this is the great surprise of resiliency in that it is common rather than uncommon among people. The human system of adaptation is an ordinary phenomenon: "What began as a quest to understand the extraordinary has revealed the power of the ordinary. Resilience does not come from rare and special qualities, but from the everyday magic of ordinary, normative human resources in the minds, brains, and bodies of children, in their families and relationships, and in their communities" (p. 235).

RESILIENCE AS HARDINESS

Hardiness is a psychological construct that is composed of three interrelated components: *control* or believing that one has influence over life events; *commitment* or feeling strongly involved in one's life, relationships, oneself and activities; and *challenge* or the capacity to experience stressful and adverse events as challenges (Maddi, 2008). Hardiness has been associated with appraisal of negative events as being less threatening, a more optimistic appraisal of ability to cope with stressful situations, and increased resistance to developing PTSD. In a recent book by Stein and Bartone (2020), the three dimensions of hardiness are summarized here:

- Commitment—People high in hardiness-commitment see life as overall meaningful and worthwhile, even though it sometimes brings pain and disappointment. These kinds of people pursue their interests with vigor, are deeply involved with their work and were socially engaged with other people. They are also reflective about themselves and aware of their own feelings and reactions.
- Challenge—People high in hardiness have a strong sense of challenge: they enjoy variety and tend to see change and disruptions in life as interesting opportunities to learn and grow. In contrast, those low in challenge prefer stability and predictability in their lives and tend to avoid new and changing situations.
- Control—Control is simply the belief that your own actions make a real difference in the results that follow, that what you do has an effect on outcomes. In contrast, people low in hardiness-control generally feel powerless to control or influence events in their lives. (pp. 10–13)

Hardiness is often considered an important factor in psychological resilience (Bartone et al., 2010). Research has accumulated supporting hardiness as having buffering effects on stress. Hardiness appears to encourage mental and positive coping, social support, and self-care and health practices (Maddi, 2004). Maddi characterized hardiness as a combination of three attitudes (commitment, control, and challenge) that are needed to buffer from stress. Bartone (2010) considers hardiness as a broad personality style that includes cognitive, emotional, and behavioral qualities.

HARDINESS AND THE POLICE

Tang and Hammontree (1992) studied police officers from seven suburban police departments over a period of time. High hardy police officers with a high level of police stress tended to have a higher level of absenteeism than officers with a low level of police stress, whereas low hardy officers experienced a high level of absenteeism regardless of their level of police stress. Of interest in this study were results concerning associations between psychological distress and hardiness. Results suggested that hardiness *overall* may be less effective in police work for ameliorating psychological distress than the individual hardiness dimensions of commitment and control. These results also suggested further consideration of the protective impact of hardiness on PTSD symptoms and depression in police.

Another study by Allison et al. (2020) looked at chronic exposure to occupational stress, depressive symptoms, coping, and hardiness among police officers. Results indicated that that work stressors involving physical/psychological threat, administrative/organizational pressure and lack of support were associated with higher symptoms of depression. High passive (negative style) coping and low active coping (positive style) was associated with higher depressive symptom scores. Stratification by hardiness revealed higher hardiness to be protective against depression. The commitment dimension of hardiness had the greatest effect in terms of moderating the association between stress and depression—those with high commitment had the lowest depressive symptom scores overall. The control dimension also modified the association, but effect modification was not found with the challenge hardiness component. People with high commitment are more likely to find meaning in an event, have a strong sense of commitment to goals and involvement with other people, which may help them better cope with stress (Fyhn et al., 2016). Similarly, a high sense of control indicates that the officer feels like they can manage the stress. This is also consistent with other research that indicated that a sense of control increases a sense of esteem and worth as well as life satisfaction and personal growth, which likely buffers symptoms of depression (Eschleman et al., 2010).

Resiliency is enhanced by support. Support from family members, friends, co-workers, and organizations are thought to be important factors for increasing resiliency in the prevention and treatment of PTSD (Whealin, Ruzek, & Southwick, 2008). This has been verified in studies involving various populations including returning veterans, victims of violent crime and victims of serious motor vehicle accidents (Pietrzak, Goldstein, Malley, Rivers, & Southwick, 2010; Tsai, Harpaz-Rotem, Pietrzak, & Southwick, 2012). Symptoms from exposure to traumatic events can be disturbing to members of an individual's social group, potentially leaving them in relative social isolation. Peer support groups who understand the nature of trauma symptoms can be helpful in providing social support and a feeling of being understood (Tsai et al., 2012).

Active (positive) styles of coping and the commitment and control dimensions of hardiness may be viable protective factors associated with reducing the adverse effects of occupational stress and depressive symptoms in law enforcement. Early training on coping skills may help young officers manage the effects of work stressors more effectively while they gain experience in police work. While hardiness is a personality trait, it may be beneficial for officers to become familiar with the concept in the context of police work.

AN EXPERIMENT TO INCREASE RESILIENCE IN POLICE OFFICERS

Proactive training in resilience is important in police work to help reduce the impact of future stress and trauma. An example of a resilience intervention was conducted by Arnetz et al. (2009). This intervention was based on combining structured relaxation methods and rehearsal of skills for dealing with known police work stressors with the goal of achieving "optimal focus, effective weapons management, and navigating novel environments during a critical incident" (Arnetz et al., 2009). The purpose of the Arnetz experiment was to prepare officers to successfully cope with job-related stress and trauma. This prevention program was unique because it:

- Targeted primary prevention, i.e., before professionals develops mental health symptoms.
- Combined emotional skills regulation training with improved operational and tactical skills to handle professional-derived trauma and challenges.
- Demonstrated sustained benefits over a 2-year follow-up period, substantially longer than any prior controlled trauma-prevention study.

Components of the Arnetz et al. (2009) sessions:

- Relaxation training,
- Guided imagery training to facilitate imaginal exposure to potentially stressful events,
- Mental practice of police tactical skills,
- Adaptive coping strategies for the different scenarios,
- Educational presentation that included discussion of the theory of stress,
- Impact on health and performance,
- Muscle relaxation technique,
- Homework to practice the relaxation technique daily was assigned.

Participants met once per week in small groups with their police group leader for 90-minute sessions for nine consecutive weeks. The leader began each session with a review of the previous week's session and homework assignment. Over the next 60 minutes, two police-relevant stress scenarios were presented. The presentation included exposure to critical incident police work scenarios via narrated, present-tense scenarios and guided imagery that was read aloud by the group leader. The group then practiced an abbreviated, 15-minute version of the relaxation techniques. Officers not only had exposure-based preparation for potential duty-related incidents but also learned job skills and increased predictability of their job in order to promote successful adjustment to future trauma exposures.

Examples of scenarios:

- A threatening situation while alone in a room
- Active robbery with gunshots
- Domestic violence where children are adversely affected
- Death involving a child
- Facing a threatening situation not really knowing what a suspect is carrying in his hands
- Meeting an armed suspect with a gun face-to-face
- High-speed car chase
- Traffic accidents with multiple car involvement and with severely injured persons
- Experiencing another police officer in a life-threatening situation

Each scenario was described in great detail with vivid imagery to ensure that participants developed vivid, lifelike mental images during the scenario, were emotionally engaged and physiologically aroused. The imaginal training was designed to increase participants' familiarity with potential future trauma and stressors, which is expected to increase their cognitive processing efficiency when applying their skills to similar situations on the job. Officers had lower levels of negative mood after the simulated critical incident and lower autonomic reactivity, as measured by increase from baseline heart rate, during the simulated critical incident. Objective observations of police performance during the incident were higher for the training group (Arnetz, 2009).

BUILDING RESILIENCE IN POLICE OFFICERS: ORGANIZATIONAL STRATEGIES

First: What are Some Problems with Establishing Resilient Police Organizations?

- No indication of an organizational culture of readiness or resilience.
- Resilience does have high priority for leadership or is supported.
- Officers not feeling heard or not feeling like an integral part of the organization.
- Trust is fractured throughout the department, including trust in leadership and trust in the organization as a whole.
- Officers not aware of the resources or programs available to them, do not use them, and do not feel that policies to support them are in place.
- Communication is lacking in many ways. Best practices are generally not discussed or shared within or among components. There is a lack of communication about resources and programs available to staff, their input is not sought, and their accomplishments are not celebrated.

Second: What Does A Resilient Police Department Look Like?

- Trained with the knowledge, skills, and attitudes required to perform the mission.

- Properly equipped with tools and protective assets to support the mission.
- Healthy and fit to endure the environmental conditions required in the mission.
- Guided by strong and effective leaders.
- Is ready to perform its roles and missions.
- Withstands and copes with stress.
- Adapts and adjusts to challenging conditions.
- Rebounds and grows from experience (Institute of Medicine, 2013).

Third: What Can Be Done?

The Officer Safety and Wellness Group formed by Office of Community Oriented Policing Services (COPS) held a meeting in 2017 to formulate ideas for increasing resilience among police officers (Spence, 2017). Maintaining health was a key factor. Dr. Jon Sheinberg at the COPS meeting proposed the following pillars should be given high priority in every law enforcement agency as the building blocks of resilience:

- Tactical trauma care. Law enforcement agencies must have standardized equipment, including trauma care kits, and training in tactical trauma care such as hemorrhage control. When an officer is shot, the first responder to the scene is often a fellow officer.
- Cardiac screening. The risk of heart disease appears higher among police officers than the general population and may be exacerbated by the acute surge of adrenaline that officers experience in critical incidents. Screening for potential heart problems is necessary, relatively inexpensive, and likely to save money in the long run.
- Fitness. Lack of fitness is a health risk for officers and a liability for their agencies. Every agency should have fitness standards for all of its officers. In addition, agencies should have consequences—though not necessarily punitive—for failure to meet the standards and a benefit or reward structure for those who meet or exceed them.
- Overweight and obesity. The risk of shift work and having a sedentary job places law enforcement officers at higher risk of

being overweight or obese, both of which increase the risk of heart disease and stroke and make the law enforcement officer less successful in certain job-related performance measures.

- Emotional or mental health. On a daily basis, law enforcement officers see small traumas that, over time, can have as significant an impact as a major incident. This can lead to a higher risk of self-medicating behaviors such as alcohol use. (p. 26.)

The COPS meeting (Spence, 2017) also suggested the following organizational strategies:

- Don't just launch new initiatives. Inventory what the agency has and assess what it needs. This also includes educating everyone in the agency on key facts and data about officer health and wellness. For example, talk about the rates and circumstances of officer suicides, heart attacks, obesity, line-of-duty injuries and deaths, vehicular crashes, and other basic awareness facts that everyone in the profession should know.
- Involve the whole agency in establishing wellness programs. The best programs involve management and rank and file working together and include education, screening, and service provision. Wellness does not need to be a chore, and programs can include incentives and competition to help inspire self-care.
- Provide a variety of options to help officers address their emotional health needs effectively. Formal counseling services are one avenue but so too are chaplaincy programs, peer support programs, mentoring, and information on other venues for assistance.
- Model good behavior and take ownership of initiatives. Agency leaders need to be clear that nothing is more important than the wellness of officers; this realization includes leaders' own wellness. Show a commitment to diet, fitness, physical and emotional health screenings, body armor, and seatbelts when asking officers to do the same.
- Make fitness fun. Building teams and a sense of community within the agency can not only improve individual health but also make fitness enjoyable. Remember that the common use of push-ups as discipline in the academy may work to influence behavior during training, but that method also likely ensures

that those officers will never do a push-up again once they graduate.

- Provide officers with annual fitness evaluations, regular information on the health risks of inadequate sleep, ongoing nutritional counseling, and periodic cardiac screening. Although providing a full cardiovascular risk assessment for all officers would be the ideal approach, even small steps can help. An agency should consult with knowledgeable experts to ensure the agency uses good, validated tests; otherwise, the money is not well spent.
- Talk about trauma as an experience shared by community members and law enforcement officers. This trauma-informed approach could help improve trust between the community and officers. Making agencies trauma-informed does not mean making officers feel like victims; rather, it is about recognizing and validating the trauma officers' experience.
- Collect and analyze national data to identify the characteristics of successful officers to help define the characteristics associated with resilience. For example, one attendee said that individuals who succeeded at his workplace were more likely to have played team sports in high school and college. The more we understand about individual resilience, the more we can do to promote and protect it.
- Remember the influence survivors can have on current officers. Messages like "take care of yourself" hold a lot of weight when they come from survivors.
- Create a system to collect resilience research results and use the research to build effective programs. Currently, law enforcement experts recommend wellness programs without having the data to show if the programs are effective.
- Create comprehensive officer safety and wellness toolkits. These tool kits should include resources that cover issues such as the long-term effects of doing law enforcement work and how officers can take care of themselves to counteract those effects. There should be toolkits for agencies as well as for individuals. Resilient agencies empower officers to take ownership of their own health and wellness.
- Push for a major cultural shift within law enforcement that talks about all five pillars of resilience. (pp. 41-43.)

LEADERSHIP: A KEY FACTOR FOR
RESILIENT POLICE ORGANIZATIONS

Leadership is critical for building individual and organizational resilience. Support by high-ranking leaders and others throughout the leadership ranks is an important building block for both initiating change (Everly, 2013). A culture of leadership is necessary to create a culture of resilience, and developing resilient leaders is crucial in creating this culture. (Everly, 2013).

Leaders play an important role in developing and sustaining empowering environments (Liden, Wayne, & Sparrowe, 2000). This helps officers to plan and respond to stress and trauma at work. Leadership practices such as positive reinforcement help create an empowering team environment (Manz & Sims, 1987; Paton, 1994), particularly when they focus on discussion of response problems to trauma and stress and how they can be resolved in the future (Quinn & Spreitzer, 1997). The role of the leader in focusing on positive outcomes related to traumatic incidents helps to alleviate fear of future trauma at work and to develop active and workable approaches to such trauma (Paton & Stephens, 1996).

According to Bartone et al. (2002), the leader who communicates a positive construction of stressful experiences may exert influence on workers to move in a positive direction when faced with stress and trauma. Resilient leaders are therefore more likely have a greater impact in their groups under high stress conditions. The success of any organization and the execution of its programs depend on effective leadership. That is true of a successful resilience program. In this challenging time for police—with their severe budget cuts, furloughs, pay freezes, and reduced resources—leadership is especially important not only for absorbing and managing employees' uncertainty about the future but for engaging employees, deepening their organizational commitment, and increasing general job satisfaction.

Resilient leaders are important in developing resilient officers because:

• Leadership is the single most critical factor in the success or failure of institutions (Bass & Bass, 2009, p. 11).
• Leadership has been shown to influence employee morale, productivity, job satisfaction, organizational commitment, stress, and resilience (Cunniff, 2013; Everly, 2013).

- When leadership is effective, it can create "a climate of trust, growth and development, which can enhance performance" (Bates et al., 2010, p. 33).
- Poor leaders and lack of supervisor social support can have adverse effects on employees (Kelloway et al., 2005).
- Poor leaders increase stress and contribute to other stressors in the workplace, including workload and pace, role conflict and ambiguity, career concerns, work scheduling, interpersonal relations, job content, and control (Kelloway et al., 2005).
- Ineffective leadership can also lead to decreased organizational commitment and high turnover rates in an organization. According to Ganter (2012) people leave organizations when their supervisors and leaders do not "create a sense of purpose, hope, direction, and trust" (Gantner, 2012).

RESILENCY AND ORGANIZATIONAL SUPPORT

Police resilience depends on police officers capacity to render challenging experiences manageable and requires the interaction of person and organization (Paton, 2008). Stress and trauma cannot be handled alone and resilience and adaptive capacity depend on support and cohesion. Integration of person and organizational factors develop and sustain police officer resilience, with the organizational level having the greatest influence on sustaining resilience. This argument is based on the fact that the police organization defines the context within which officers experience and interpret critical incidents and their sequelae and within which future capabilities are nurtured or restricted (Paton, 2006).

Trust is a crucial determinant of the effectiveness of interpersonal relationships, group processes and organizational relationships (Barker & Camarata, 1998; Herriot, Hirch & Reilly, 1998) and plays a crucial role in developing resilient officers (Spreitzer & Mishra, 1999). Unfortunately, there is a lack of trust between police administration and officers who work in day-to-day policing (Shane, 2010). The goal of police organizations should move toward establishing an increased trust among workers. Trust has been identified as a predictor of people's ability to deal with complex, high risk events (Siegrist & Cvetkovich, 2000), particularly when relying on others to provide information or assistance. An officer is more willing to commit to acting cooperatively in high risk situations when they believe those with whom they must collaborate or work under are competent, dependable, and trusting (Dirks, 1999).

Eranen, Millar and Paton (1999) demonstrated that perceptions of organizational climate was the most important predictor of stress responses. Paton, Smith, Ramsay and Akande (1999) demonstrated that organizational characteristics superseded event characteristics as determinants of traumatic stress reactions among firefighters. Alexander and Wells (1991) concluded that a supportive managerial culture played a prominent role in facilitating resilience in police offers performing body recovery duties. Hart and Wearing (1995) demonstrated that the dominant influence on both stress and well-being in police officers was organizational rather than operational. Organizational structure, procedures and culture exercise a powerful influence on how adverse events are experienced. Interventions should be proactive and established prior to exposure (e.g., through selection, training, organizational development), rather than reactive. In this way, intervention can be truly preventative, increase staff capability to bounce back from encounters with adversity, and facilitate the likelihood that such exposure will enrich their personal and professional lives.

In conclusion, resilience in police work results from the interaction between person and organization. Because police officers encounter unpredictable and challenging circumstances repeatedly, it is important that resilience programs are designed as learning strategies that facilitate the development of an officers' capacity to adapt to unpredictable circumstances. It is difficult to go it alone when individuals are exposed to stress and trauma on a daily basis such as police officers are.

Discussion in this chapter ranged from definitions of resilience to factors which can enhance individual officers through organizational participation and support. Resiliency may be person centered to some degree, but even the most resilient officer needs support from the organization. Additionally, as Southwick et al. (2015) point out, no two people are exactly alike and that determinants of resilience may vary. The suggestions offered in this chapter to increase resilience in police just scratch the surface. More research is needed in what works best in this occupation. We move now to the next chapter where we look for new directions in police mental and physical health.

REFERENCES

Allison, P., Mnatsakanova, A., McCanlies, E., Fekedulegn, D., Hartley, T. A., Andrew, M. E., & Violanti, J. M. (2019). Police stress and depressive symptoms: role of coping and hardiness. *Policing (Bradford, England), 43*(2), 247–261. https://doi.org/10.1108/pijpsm-04-2019-0055

Alexander, D. A., & Wells, A. (1991). Reactions of police officers to body handling after a major disaster: A before and after comparison. *British Journal of Psychiatry, 159,* 517–555.

Andrew, M. E., McCanlies, E. C., Burchfiel, C. M., Charles, L., Hartley, T. A., Fekedulegn, D., & Violanti, J. M. (2008). Hardiness and psychological distress in a cohort of police officers. *International Journal of Emergency Mental Health, 10*(2), 137–148.

American Psychological Association. (2014). *The road to resilience.* Washington, DC: American Psychological Association. Retrieved from http://www.apa.org/help center/road-resilience.asp

Andrew, M. E., Howsare J. L., Hartley, T. A., McCanlies, E. C., Burchfiel, C. M., & Violanti J. M. (2014). Protective attributes: resilience in policing. In J. M. Violanti (Ed.), *Dying for the job: Police work exposure and health.* Springfield, IL: Charles C Thomas, Publisher, Ltd., pp. 145–154.

Arnetz, B. B., Nevedal, D. C., Lumley, M. A., Backman, L., & Lublin, A. (2009). Trauma resilience training for police: Psychophysiological and performance effects. *Journal of Police and Criminal Psychology, 24*(1), 1–9. https://doi.org/10.1007/s11896-008-9030-y

Barker, R. T., & Camarata, M. R. (1998). The role of communication in creating and maintaining a learning organization: Preconditions, indicators, and disciplines. *Journal of Business Communication, 35,* 443–467.

Bartone, P. T., Snook, S. A., & Tremble, Jr., T. R. (2002). Cognitive and personality predictors of leader performance in West Point cadets. *Military Psychology, 14*(4), 321–338. doi: 10.1207/S15327876MP1404_6

Bartone, P. T. (2006). Resilience under military operational stress: Can leaders influence hardiness? *Military Psychology, 18*(Suppl), S131–S148. https://doi.org/10.1207/s15327876mp1803s_10

Bass, B. M., & Bass, R. (2009). *The bass handbook of leadership: Theory, research, and managerial applications.* New York: Free Press, p. 11.

Cunniff, E. (2013). *Leadership in large and complex organizations.* Presentation to the IOM Committee on Department of Homeland Security Workforce Resilience, February 4–5, Washington, DC.

Dirks, K. T. (1999). The effects of interpersonal trust on work group performance. *Journal of Applied Psychology, 34,* 445–455

Eranen, L., Millar, M., & Paton, D. (1999). *Organisational recovery from disaster: Traumatic response within voluntary disaster workers.* Paper presented at the International Society for Stress Studies Conference, June 6, 1999, Istanbul.

Eschleman, K. J., Bowling, N. A., & Alarcon, G. M. (2010). A meta-analytic examination of hardiness. *International Journal of Stress Management, 17,* 277–307. 10.1037/a0020476

Everly, G., Smith, K. J., & Lobo, R. (2013). Resilient leadership and the organizational culture of resilience: Construct validation. *International Journal of Emergency Mental Health, 15*(2), 123–128.

Fyhn, T., Fjell, K. K., & Johnsen, B. H. (2016). Resilience factors among police investigators: Hardiness-commitment a unique contributor. *Journal of Police and Criminal Psychology, 31,* 261–269. https://doi.org/10.1007/s11896-015-9181-6

Gantner, R. K. 2012. *Workplace wellness: Performance with a purpose.* Moon Township, PA: Well Works Publishing.

Hart, P. M., Wearing, A.. & Headey, B. (1993). Assessing police work experiences: Development of the police daily hassles and uplifts scales. *Journal of Criminal Justice, 21,* 553–572.

Herriot, P., Hirsh, W., & Reilly, P. (1998). *Trust and transition: Managing today's employment relationship.* Chichester: John Wiley & Sons.

Hystad, S. W., Eid, J., Johnsen, B. H., Laberg, J. C., & Bartone, P. (2010). Psychometric properties of the revised Norwegian dispositional resilience (hardiness) scale. *Scandinavian Journal of Psychology, 51*(3), 237–245. https://doi.org /10.1111/j.1467-9450.2009.00759.x

Institute of Medicine. (2013). *A ready and resilient workforce for the Department of Homeland Security: Protecting America's front line.* Washington, DC: The National Academies Press. https://doi.org/10.17226/18407

Kelloway, E. K., Sivanathan, N., Francis, L., & Barling, J. (2005). Poor leadership. *Handbook of Work Stress.* New York: Sage, pp. 89–112.

Liden, R. C., Wayne, S. J., & Sparrowe, R. T. (2000). An examination of the mediating role of psychological empowerment on the relations between the job, interpersonal relationships, and work outcomes. *Journal of Applied Psychology, 85*(3), 407–416. https://doi.org/10.1037/0021-9010.85.3.407

Maddi, S. R. (2004). Hardiness: An operationalization of existential courage. *Journal of Humanistic Psychology, 44*(3), 279–298. doi: 10.1177/0022167804266101

Manz, C. C., & Sims, H. P. Jr. (1987). Leading workers to lead themselves. The external leadership of self-managing work teams. *Administrative Science Quarterly, 32,* 106–129.

Masten, A. (2001). Ordinary magic: Resilience processes in development. *American Psychologist, 56*(3), 227–238. doi: 10.1037//0003-066X.56.3.227

Paton, D., & Stephens, C. (1996). Training and support for emergency responders. In D. Paton & J. M. Violanti (Eds.), *Traumatic stress in critical occupations: Recognition, consequences and treatment* (pp. 173–205). Springfield, IL: Charles C Thomas, Publisher, Ltd.

Paton, D., Smith, L. M., Ramsay, R., & Akande, D. (1999). A structural re-assessment of the Impact of Event Scale: The influence of occupational and cultural contexts. In R. Gist & B. Lubin (Eds.), *Response to disaster.* Philadelphia: Taylor & Francis, pp. 83–100.

Paton, D., Violanti, J. M., & Smith, L. M. (Eds.). (2003). *Promoting capabilities to manage posttraumatic stress: Perspectives on resilience.* Springfield, IL: Charles C Thomas, Publisher, Ltd., pp. 3–7.

Paton, D. (2006). Posaraurriatic growth in emergency professionals. In L. Calhoun & R. Tedeschi (Eds.), *Handbook of posttraumatic growth: Research and practice.* Mahwah, NJ: Lawrence Erlbaum Associates.

Paton, D., & Violanti, J. M. (2008). Law enforcement response to terrorism: The role of the resilient police organization. *International Journal of Emergency Mental Health, 102,* 125–136.

Pietrzak, R. H., Johnson, D. C., Goldstein, M. B., Malley, J. C., & Southwick, S. M. (2009). Psychological resilience and post-deployment social support protect against traumatic stress and depressive symptoms in soldiers returning from Operations Enduring Freedom and Iraqi Freedom. *Depression and Anxiety, 26*(8), 745–751. https://doi.org/10.1002/da.20558

Phelan, J. C., Lucas, J. W., Ridgeway, C. L., & Taylor, C. J. (2014). Stigma, status, and population health. *Social Science & Medicine (1982), 103,* 15–23. https://doi.org/10.1016/j.socscimed.2013.10.004

Quinn, R. E., & Spreitzer, G. M. (1997). The road to empowerment: Seven questions every leader should consider. *Organizational Dynamics, 26*(2), 37–49. https://doi.org/10.1016/S0090-2616(97)90004-8

Shane, J. M. (2010). Organizational stressors and police performance. *Journal of Criminal Justice, 38*(4), 807–818. https://doi.org/10.1016/j.jcrimjus.2010.05.008

Siegrist, M., & Cvetkovich, G. (2000). Perception of hazards: The role of social trust and knowledge. *Risk Analvsis, 20,* 713–719.

Southwick, S. M., Bonanno, G. A., Masten, A. S., Panter-Brick, C., & Yehuda, R. (2014). Resilience definitions, theory, and challenges: Interdisciplinary perspectives. *European Journal of Psychotraumatology,* Oct. 1;5 (525338). doi:10.3402/ejpt.v5.25338

Southwick, S. M., Pietrzak, R. H., Tsai, J., Krystal, J. H., & Charney, D. (2015). Resilience: An update. *PTSD Research Quarterly, 25*(4), 1–4.

Spence, D. (Ed.). (2017). *Improving law enforcement resilience: Lessons and recommendations.* Officer Safety and Wellness Group Meeting Summary. Washington, DC: Office of Community Oriented Policing Services, pp. 26, 41–43.

Spreitzer, G. M., & Mishra, A. K. (1999). Giving up control without losing control: Trust and its substitutes' effect on managers involving employees in decision making. *Group & Organization Management, 24,* 155–187.

Stein, S. J., & Bartone, P. T. (2020). *Hardiness: Making stress work for you to achieve your life goals.* Hoboken, NJ: Wiley, pp. 10–13.

Tang, T. L., & Hammontree, M. L. (1992). The effects of hardiness, police stress, and life stress on police officers' illness and absenteeism. *Public Personnel Management, 21*(4), 493–510. https://doi.org/10.1177/009102609202100406

Tsai, J., Harpaz-Rotem, I., Pietrzak, R. H., & Southwick, S. M. (2012). The role of coping, resilience, and social support in mediating the relation between PTSD and social functioning in veterans returning from Iraq and Afghanistan. *Psychiatry, 75*(2), 135–149. https://doi.org/10.1521/psyc.2012.75.2.135

Whealin, J. M., Ruzek, J. I., & Southwick, S. (2008). Cognitive-behavioral theory and preparation for professionals at risk for trauma exposure. *Trauma, Violence, & Abuse, 9*(2), 100–113. https://doi.org/10.1177/1524838008315869

Chapter 6

WHERE DO WE GO FROM HERE? FUTURE CONSIDERATIONS

Hope itself is like a star—not to be seen in the sunshine of prosperity, and only to be discovered in the night of adversity.
—Charles Haddon Spurgeon

LEGISLATING POLICE MENTAL HEALTH: A GOOD START

Recent legislature has provided a good first step to address the mental health crisis in law enforcement. The Law Enforcement Mental Health and Wellness Act (2018) (LEMHWA) outlines the need to make police departments aware of this problem and provides funding to help reduce mental health issues among officers.

LEMHWA called for the U.S. Department of Justice (DOJ) to submit a report to Congress on mental health practices and services in the U.S. Departments of Defense and Veterans Affairs (VA) that could be adopted by federal, state, local, or tribal law enforcement agencies as well as a report containing recommendations to Congress on:

- Effectiveness of crisis lines for law enforcement officers;
- Efficacy of annual mental health checks for law enforcement officers;
- Expansion of peer mentoring programs;
- Ensuring privacy considerations for these types of programs.

LEMHWA specified that this work should include identifying and reviewing research as well as consulting with state, local, and tribal law enforcement agencies; the U.S. Department of Homeland Security (DHS); and other federal agencies that employ law enforcement

111

officers. The act also specified that the Director of the Office of Community Oriented Policing Services (COPS Office) would submit a report to Congress that focuses on case studies of programs designed primarily to address officer psychological health and well-being.

Another step forward for suicide prevention in police work is the Law Enforcement Suicide Data Collection Act which requires the director of the Federal Bureau of Investigation to provide information on suicide rates in law enforcement and for other purposes. This act will help departments and researchers to determine the actual scope of the police suicide problem and provide insight to etiology.

In summary, the Law Enforcement Suicide Data Collection Act states that the attorney general, acting through the director of the Federal Bureau of Investigation, shall establish a program for the purpose of preventing future law enforcement suicides and promoting understanding of suicide in law enforcement. Law enforcement agencies may submit to the FBI, and the FBI must report on, data about suicides and attempted suicides within such law enforcement agencies, including information on:

- The circumstances and events that occurred before each suicide or attempted suicide;
- The general location of each suicide or attempted suicide;
- The demographic information of each law enforcement officer who commits or attempts suicide;
- The occupational category, including criminal investigator, corrections officer, line of duty officer, 911 dispatch operator, of each law enforcement officer who commits or attempts suicide;
- The method used in each suicide or attempted suicide.

Not later than two years after the date of enactment of this act, and annually thereafter, the attorney general, acting through the director of the Federal Bureau of Investigation, shall submit to Congress and publish on the website of the Federal Bureau of Investigation a report containing the information submitted to the director. The report described under subsection may not include any personally identifiable information of a law enforcement officer who commits or attempts suicide (134 STAT. 644 PUBLIC LAW 116-143–JUNE 16, 2020 Public Law 116-143 116th Congress, June 16, 2020). Approved June 16, 2020).

INTERVENTIONS: ENHANCING POLICE HEALTH

Physical and mental health are adversely affected by exposures and lifestyle factors in police work, and many factors related to stress, mental health, and cardiovascular disease outcomes have increased over time. The interventions discussed below are examples of potential strategies to help mitigate stress and adverse health outcomes among police.

The Need for Police Wellness Programs

Increasing health care costs and rates of premature disease and death have produced a wellness movement across the nation. More than two-thirds of premature deaths are caused by risk factors such as smoking, poor diet, and lack of exercise (Hampl, Anderson, & Mullis, 2002). Heart disease, cancer, and stroke represent the three leading causes of death among adults in the United States. Statistics indicate that 60% of factors impacting premature death are based on a combination of social/environmental factors (20%) and behavior (40%) (CDC, 2020). Mental health professionals need to first understand and consider the unique culture of law enforcement. Such research efforts should incorporate the professional assistance of various mental health professionals who work in the field of law enforcement and who have frequent contact with personnel in law enforcement, as well as a well-developed understanding of the inherent struggles, challenges, and needs in police work (Tanagoshi et al., 2008).

Many police organizations have begun to place an increased emphasis on wellness, healthy lifestyle behaviors and prevention efforts. Example: A wellness program initiated by the Seminole County, Florida Sheriff's department in 2016, called "*Operation Thrive Wellness Challenge*" (O'Malley & Nice, 2016), has shown success in improving the health of officers. The program involved seven steps to initiate, develop, run and assess the program. Officers are surveyed to determine their wellness interests, command staff approves the program, and officers participate along with periodic health screenings. Points are earned for successfully practicing four key healthy habits (exercise, nutrition, sleep and stress management) and/or losing weight. Law enforcement specific wellness tips, strategies and support are e-mailed every week for eight weeks. Through this annual wellness challenge, agencies can expect employees to achieve measurable success in the following areas:

- Healthy weight loss
- Reduced risk of heart disease from increased self-monitoring of blood pressure and increased exercise
- Reduced risk of diabetes from improved nutrition
- Improved alertness and reaction time from improved sleep
- Improved health awareness from increased participation in biometric health screenings
- Improved morale from the inherently fun teamwork.

Kuehl et al. (2016) developed and tested the "Safety & Health Improvement: Enhancing Law Enforcement Departments" (SHIELD) program for police. The program consisted of twelve 30-minute, team-based, scripted, peer-led sessions for six months. Team meetings were scheduled once per week, and members would discuss weekly goals aloud regarding successful strategies to reach the weekly goal such as exercise, diet and sleep. Kuehl et al. (2016) base the success of the program on the team approach, which encouraged competition and peer pressure to succeed. The program was found to be effective at six months in improving diet, sleep, stress, and overall quality of life of law enforcement department personnel. Long-term effects were observed for consumption of fruits and vegetables, and there was some evidence for effects on tobacco and alcohol use. Assessment of dietary habits, physical activity behaviors, weight loss maintenance, and substance use is rare more than one year following an intervention, and in general, initial positive changes do not persist in prior research (Kuehl et al., 2016).

A wellness plan was developed by the National Institute of Justice (NIJ) (National Institute of Justice, 2016–2021) to improve the safety, health, and wellness of those working in the criminal justice system. There are seven objectives to the plan:

- Promote research to improve the physical and mental health of individuals working in the criminal justice system.
- Study both trauma and suicide among criminal justice employees.

- Assess the impact of criminal justice work stressors on the families of individuals employed in the criminal justice system.
- Promote science-based tools and strategies to monitor physical and mental health.
- Reduce suicide and self-harm in corrections, with a specific focus on jails.
- Assess the effect of in-custody conditions on physical and mental health and the impact of these conditions on preparing these individuals for reintegration in the community.
- Promote scientifically based tools and strategies to monitor physical and mental health of individuals under the supervision of the criminal justice system.

The Police Organization: The Need for Change

Over decades of research, organizational stressors have been reported as a significant source of stress among police officers (Crank & Caldero, 1991; Shane, 2010). This source of stress includes inadequate support from supervisors, lack of control over workload, poor management practices, and other aspects of the organization and behaviors of its personnel (Shane, 2010). Organizational stressors may constitute the greatest source of stress due to their prevalence in police work and/or the perception because they are perceived as uncontrollable, unnecessary, and unavoidable sources of stress (Purba & Demou, 2019). In terms of mental health, Purba and Demou (2019) found that organizational stress in police work contributes to depression, anxiety, burnout, suicidal ideation, and other adverse mental well-being outcomes. Purba and Demou (2019) identified thirty-six different police organizational stressors among fifteen articles and found that twenty-five of the thirty-six were significant predictors of mental well-being outcomes. Organizational stress was most closely associated with psychiatric symptoms/psychological distress, emotional exhaustion, and depersonalization.

Violanti et al. (2016) and Tyagi and Dhar, (2014) found that organizational stressors were ranked as both stressful and prevalent. Cooper et al. (1982) suggested that organizational stressors were significant predictors of Type A behavior, which was described as an indicator of cardiovascular health and a strong predictor of cardiovascular disease. Recent research lends support to the conclusion that organizational stress may be contributing to cardiovascular-related morbidity and mortality (Zimmerman, 2012). Collins et al. (2005), for example, found that job strain and low decision latitude are associated with reductions in cardiac vagal control during working hours in a sample of healthy middle-aged males. Andrew et al. (2017) found that perceived lack of support was associated with compromised cardiac vagal control among officers that participated in the BCOPS study, further suggesting cardiovascular problems associated with organizational stress. There remain many questions on whether organizational stress in policing is associated with immune system functioning, cancer rates, neurological disorders, cortisol response, oxidative stress, and other pathologies. These pathologies have been associated with operational stress, but the effects of organizational stress remain largely unknown (Hartley et al., 2011).

Suggestions for Organizational Change

Burke (2017) suggested that stress reduction is based on worksite changes and changing the orientation of individual officers by education and increasing personal resilience. Leiter and Maslach (2004) suggest reducing stress with organizational changes that increase the balance between effort and reward. They suggested allowing more control, acknowledging accomplishments, fairness, and financial balance. On the individual level, Leiter (1992) suggests that the selection process of new personnel should include an assessment of psychological and coping skills along with indoctrination training to help them to deal with stress.

Organizational openness is an important trait that enhances resilience against stress. Leaders who communicate openly and often help to create a supporting staff are more successful at achieving and/or maintaining a lower stress environment. Communication and openness is important across every level of the organization from the chief on down. As discussed in previous chapters, leadership practices such as positive reinforcement, positive feedback, encouragement and constructive discussion of response problems, and how they can be resolved in the future help to reduce stress risk (Paton, 1994). Organizations can help to increase resistance to stress by (1) establishing a trust between the organization and individual, (2) openness, and (3) cohesion. When dealing with stressful encounters, officers become more reliant on others for information and guidance about how to respond. Being able to turn to the organization for guidance and support helps officers to deal with stressful encounters. Trust is a prominent determinant of the effectiveness of interpersonal relationships, group processes and organizational relationships (Barker & Camarata, 1998), particularly when individuals face the constant array of stressors that police face. When dealing with stressful encounters officers have to deal with risk and uncertainty, and trust can be a powerful ally when dealing with complex high risk events (Siegrist & Cvetkovich, 2000), especially when relying on others to provide information or assistance about such experiences.

A cohesive work environment allows for sharing of knowledge and skills. One might consider cohesion to be a psychological safety net. This brings a sense of empowerment to the officer. Officers who are empowered by the organization anticipate positive rather than negative outcomes to stressful events at work. They are more likely to approach incidents as learning experiences, and this predisposition reduces stress risk (Paton et al., 2000). Success in stress reduction is likely to depend on a positive stance toward officers instead of punishment-centered bureaucratic policies. Police organizations can change the course of individual reaction from pathogenic stress to adaptation. Paton, Smith, Violanti and Eranen (2000) suggest that social cohesion among officers and the organization could act to cognitively integrate the stressful experience.

PEER SUPPORT

A viable preventive approach in policing is the development of a peer support program. Peer support can be defined as a system of giving and receiving help founded on key principles of respect, shared responsibility, and mutual agreement of what is helpful (Mead, Hilton & Curtis, 2001). Peer support will allow distressed officers to initially talk with other officers trained in basic counseling and afterwards seek professional help if necessary. An assumption underlying peer support is that trained police peers are more trusted by officers in distress than are mental health professionals (Landers & Zhou, 2011). Police peer supporters draw on their shared experiences in order to help others who are similar to them in work or life roles. Davidson et al. (1999) reported that peer support reduced symptoms for participants and increased their social integration—an important factor in suicide prevention. A potential barrier to peer support are concerns for confidentiality. This is especially strong in police work. Trust in officers who work in peer support programs is essential for success, and any peer support program can fail if trust is broken.

While peer support programs come in many different forms, they usually involve people with similar backgrounds providing emotional, social or practical support to each other. According to Solomon (2004), "peer support is social and emotional support, frequently coupled with instrumental support that is mutually offered by persons . . . sharing a similar mental health condition, to bring about a desired social or personal change." A key underlying assumption of the peer support approach is that due to shared experiences and life circumstances, peers are better able to establish connections of trust and support with those in need (Castellano, 2012). Peer support services may aim, for example, to promote hope, recovery from illness or trauma, improved life skills, psychological well-being and social integration (Landers & Zhou, 2011). Regardless of the specific program, peer supporters draw on their shared experiences in order to provide empathic understanding, information and advice to those they are helping.

Recent years have seen a rapid growth in peer support programs that aim to help people recover from a range of problems including mental and physical illness, alcohol and drug addiction, and various disabilities (Chinman et al., 2014). Peer support programs are also being applied increasingly to assist those affected by death, including family members of a military casualty, parents of a child who has died, and police and firefighters who have lost friends and co-workers (Harrington-LaMorie & Ruocco, 2011; Feigelman, Jordan, McIntosh & Feigelman, 2012; Grauwiler, Barocas & Mills, 2008).

In addition to the benefits that peer support programs provide for participants, they also appear to have similar positive effects for those serving in peer support roles (Solomon, 2004; Salzer & Shear, 2002). For example, Castellano (2012) describes a Reciprocal Peer Support model used successfully in multiple peer support programs in New Jersey in which those providing the peer support also benefit from positive recognition and affirmation of their special contributions. This is often the situation, for example, in the use of peer supporters to facilitate recovery of people with some mental illness (Chinman et al., 2014; Rittmon, 2014).

Practical Considerations: Police Peer Support

Digliani (2015, p. 3) points out that peer support in police work functions as a support and debriefing resource for employees and their families. Peer support provides support to personnel experiencing personal and work-related stress. It also provides support during and following critical or traumatic incidents resulting from performance of duty:

- Provide peer support and facilitate peer support team debriefings within the parameters established by law, departmental policy, operational and ethical guidelines, clinical supervision, and their training.
- Attend regularly scheduled peer support team meetings and in-service training.
- Develop and maintain enhanced knowledge and skill. This includes skills in recognizing stress reactions to critical incidents and the unavoidable stressors of policing and non-work environments.
- Remain in communication with the peer support team psychologist. They engage the psychologist for clinical supervision in accordance with departmental policy and operational guidelines.
- Resolve issues or conflicts that may arise between themselves and department investigators, supervisors, or administrators by working for cooperation, understanding, and education. In cases where such resolution is not readily achieved, they contact their team coordinator and team psychologist immediately for assistance.
- Make appropriate referrals when issues exceed the parameters of peer support.
- Provide peer support services to other agencies on request and as approved through mutual-aid policies.
- Remain mindful of the trust placed in them by those who seek peer support. Peer Support Interactions:
- Are founded in similar experiences, background, or history
- Are characterized by elements of functional relationships
- Encourage exploration, empowerment, and positive change
- Avoid the creation of dependency

- Are guided by ethical and conceptual parameters
- Are different than "friends talking"
- Can be a one-time contact or ongoing
- May involve an evaluative component
- Can be part of a comprehensive professional counseling program

Digliani (2019) also developed the "Proactive Annual Check-In" (PAC) which is an interactive component of an overall stress management program consisting of an annual meeting between police employees and the police psychologist, a member of the peer support team, or other agency support person. The PAC offers the opportunity for a positive exchange of thoughts and information within a confidential setting. The Proactive Annual Check-in is comprised of six primary elements:

- Annual visit with the department psychologist, member of the Peer Support Team, or other department support person
- Confidential meeting that does not initiate any record
- No evaluation—it's a check-in, not a check-up
- There does not need to be a problem
- It's a discussion of what's happening in your life
- Participation is voluntary and encouraged

The goal of the PAC is to provide a safe, non-threatening, proactive forum for law enforcement employees to talk about their lives. It is an opportunity to exchange information with a trained support person before any significant stress-related issues arise. Following a PAC meeting, additional meetings or the initiation of a more comprehensive support program are available if needed or requested.

Digliani (2019) commented:

Some law enforcement agencies are experimenting with mandatory annual mental health check-ins while others now offer incentives for annual or even semi-annual voluntary participation (such as time-off for verified participation). In proactive programs that offer incentives for verified voluntary participation, participant confidentiality issues must be considered and satisfactorily addressed. Agencies can readily implement the Proactive Annual Check-in program by utilizing currently available support resources. Utilizing available support resources helps to minimize the cost of PAC implementation. (p. 2)

MINDFULNESS

Mindfulness may be a valuable tool for police stress and trauma mitigation. Mindfulness-based meditation, which has its roots in ancient Buddhist traditions (Kabat-Zinn, 1900), has been adapted and developed as an effective stress-reduction intervention for a range of mental health disorders (Keng et al., 2011) and medical illnesses (Arias et al., 2006). Mindfulness has been defined as "the awareness that emerges from paying attention on purpose, in the present moment, and nonjudgmentally, to the unfolding of experience moment-by-moment" (Kabat-Zinn, 2003, p. 145). Bishop and colleagues (2004) proposed a model of mindfulness with two core elements: (1) maintaining attention to the immediate experience, and (2) acceptance or orientation to experience in which thoughts, feelings and sensations that arise are accepted without excessive preoccupation with, or suppression of, the experience.

Mindfulness-Based Stress Reduction (MBSR) is a structured, time-limited, group-based intervention in which individuals are taught to pay attention to sensory, cognitive and emotional experiences occurring in the moment without fixating or ruminating on the experience or judging any part of it (Kabat-Zinn, 2003). A wealth of studies have demonstrated the positive effects of MBSR on psychological functioning in clinical populations. Keng and colleagues (2011) concluded that MBSR is an effective treatment strategy for a wide range of psychological conditions including anxiety, depression, stress, rumination, anger, psychological distress, and post-traumatic avoidance symptoms. In addition, mindfulness-based interventions have been successfully adapted for the treatment of substance use disorders including alcohol and multi-drug use (Wupperman et al., 2012).

There is emerging evidence that mindfulness training is causally related to stress reduction. Recently, Baer and colleagues (2012) assessed weekly changes in both self-reported mindfulness and perceived stress over an 8-week MBSR program and found that mindfulness predicted concurrent decreases in stress at post-treatment, providing evidence that mindfulness training exerts its positive effects through stress reduction. Mindfulness has been gaining credence in various occupational venues such as medicine (Goyal et al., 2014), the military (Johnson et al., 2014), education (Klatt, Buckworth, & Malarkey, 2009), criminal justice (Kelley & Lambert, 2012), and law enforcement settings (Bergman, Christopher, & Bowen, 2016; Chopko & Schwartz, 2013; Williams, Ciarrochi, & Deane, 2010). Additional research on police is needed using mindfulness to help in the reduction of stress and trauma.

CARDIOVASCULAR DISEASE REDUCTION

A general statement from the American Heart Association Council on Nutrition, Physical Activity and Metabolism; the American Heart Association Council on Clinical Cardiology; and the American College of Sports Medicine suggests that maintaining physical fitness through regular physical activity may help to reduce cardiac events. This is because a disproportionate number of events occur in the least physically active subjects performing unaccustomed physical activity and resonates with police populations (Thompson et al., 2007). Stressful encounters may also trigger negative physiological responses such as cardiac events. Implementation of stress-reduction programs in the workplace will help officers deal with these encounters.

A finding that the majority of on-duty police cardiac deaths occurred in younger age categories (40–50 years of age) exemplifies the need for emphasis on fitness throughout the police career (Violanti, Fekedulegn, Shi, & Andrew, 2020). The study examined trends in job-related illness deaths among law enforcement officers in the United States over a 22-year period (1997–2018). Five hundred thirty-five deaths were attributed to job-related illness during the 22-year period. Among circulatory causes, 86.7% of deaths were due to a heart attack. Heart attacks were especially prevalent among male officers 40-60 years of age, with an average age of death of 46.47 years (Barnard et al., 1973; Mittleman et al., 1993). Varvargou et al. (2014) found that sudden cardiac death among police officers was considerably higher when they were involved in activities other than routine non-emergency duties. Examples were the pursuit of suspects, physical altercations, restraints, and maintaining order in disaster situations.

PTSD MITIGATION

It is necessary for police agencies to become more proactive in reducing PTSD by providing proactive training at the basic police academy level before officers are exposed to traumatic incidents. One factor that needs to be addressed is the officer's willingness to seek help for such conditions as PTSD or depression. A shift in police culture that encourages officers to freely seek psychological services when necessary, without negative consequence, will result in healthier, more resilient officers (Wester et al., 2010). The police organization can facilitate treatment for PTSD by reducing the stigma associated with mental difficulties and increasing confidential help (Violanti, 2020).

Understanding risk factors that may interact to increase an officer's risk of developing PTSD or depression is an important step to not only prevent and treat these psychological conditions but to also reduce or prevent concomitant negative psychological and biological consequences. Research shows us that PTSD is more likely to occur in occupational groups such as the police as well as military personnel, rescue workers, ambulance drivers, and firefighters (Berger et al., 2012). Factors that are directly related to police include irregular work hours, rotating shifts, and support both inside and outside work that have also been shown to be related to PTSD (Wester et al., 2010). Because PTSD is so devastating, treating it effectively is imperative. Most treatments have three basic stages in common that have been found to increase treatment efficacy. These include (1) ensuring the officers' sense of safety by increasing their capacity to manage and control physiologic arousal, (2) helping officers process and assimilate the trauma memory, and (3) helping officers re-engage in society and social relationships (Cloitre et al., 2012). There are a number of interventions currently being used to treat PTSD. Some examples are listed below.

Assistance Animals

Persons with PTSD may benefit from one or more different types of assistance animals including a service dog, therapy dog, support dog, and companion dog (Parenti, Foreman, Meade, & Wirth, 2015). Dogs are primarily used with the military for this purpose and may be applicable to police officers as well. Benefits come in several forms such as specific work or tasks related to a disability or impairment, assistance to a professional therapist in the therapy process, direct emotional and physical comfort to the individual, and general companionship. A service dog, such as a seeing-eye dog or hearing-ear dog, has been trained to provide work or tasks related to an individual's disability.

An assistance dog is trained in basic or advanced skills to assist a health care or allied health care professional within the scope of a therapeutic treatment plan. For example, a psychologist or counselor might use dogs in a therapy session to create an opportunity to increase capacity for attachment as well as help to establish an environment of trust and acceptance. A support dog provides physical, psychiatric, or emotional support to individuals primarily in the home (Chumley, 2012). There is evidence that supports interaction between humans and animals can positively impact health and well-being (Beetz et al., 2012). Several studies have evaluated the effects of human-animal interaction on specific behavioral, psychological, and physiological indices, many of which overlap with the criterion symptoms of PTSD. For example, a meta-analysis has found that assistance animals reduce symptoms of depression (Souter & Miller, 2007). Furthermore, dogs can be trained to alleviate distractibility, anxiety, intrusive imagery, dissociation, and flashbacks (Ensminger, 2010). They also stay focused on the handler which can reduce avoidance behavior. These studies indicate that assistance dogs may positively affect individuals with PTSD.

Eye Movement Desensitization and Reprocessing (EMDR)

EMDR is based on an adaptive information-processing model which posits that much of psychological pathology associated with trauma results from incomplete processing of that event (Shapiro & Maxfield, 2002). Through an eight-phase, three-pronged protocol that addresses past, present, and future clinical issues, the client is able to process and assimilate the traumatic memory (Silver, Rogers, & Russell, 2008). EMDR processing uses dual focus of attention and alternating stimulation to help someone process disturbing memories (Shapiro, 2001; Shapiro & Forrest, 2004). This all helps the person to decrease the stress associated with traumatic event and future similar events that may trigger memories (Shapiro & Forrest, 2004). There is a large body of evidence showing that EMDR is effective for treating PTSD (Cloitre, 2009; Shapiro & Forrest, 2004; Sharpless & Barber, 2011). Meta-analyses found that in both military and civilian populations EMDR worked as well or was more effective other therapies (Cloitre, 2009; Sharpless & Barber, 2011). EMDR has also been shown to be superior to relaxation techniques, supportive counseling, and treatment as usual (Cloitre, 2009).

Prolonged Exposure (PE)

PE incorporates imaginal exposure and systematic desensitization to treat PTSD. In imaginal exposure the client is asked to imagine and recount the details of the traumatic event. This occurs progressively over many sessions. The sessions are audiotaped and the client listens to the tapes at home. As clients continue exposure therapy they report that their anxiety begins to subside and a coherent narrative is developed. Success of this procedure is dependent on emotional engagement, such as fear, but also the ability to regulate emotions so that the client does not feel panic or terror. Numerous studies have shown the efficacy of prolonged exposure for treating PTSD in both military and civilian populations (Sharpless & Barber, 2011).

Stress Inoculation Training (SIT)

SIT was originally used to manage symptoms of anxiety but was adapted to treat PTSD symptoms in sexual assault victims (Cloitre, 2009). It is composed of a number of different techniques including muscle relaxation, thought stopping, role play guided self-dialogue, and graduated exposure techniques to address symptoms of PTSD (Cloitre, 2009). Further research in larger police populations will be important to determine if this therapy is effective in first responders.

Yoga

Yoga is a client-centered practice that incorporates physical postures, regulated breathing, and meditation (Telles, Singh, & Balkrishna, 2012). A recent review evaluated eleven studies that used yoga to manage trauma associated with combat, natural disasters, interpersonal violence, and being incarcerated (Telles et al., 2012).

Yoga is currently practiced in approximately 29% of Veteran's Administration PTSD treatment programs (Libby, Reddy, Pilver, & Desai, 2012). Studies suggest that yoga may be an effective method for alleviating symptoms associated with trauma and PTSD (Bussing, Michalsen, Khalsa, Telles, & Sherman, 2012).

There are many other forms of therapy available for the treatment of PTSD that go beyond the scope of this book. They include Cognitive Behavior Therapy (CBT), Medications, Prolonged Exposure Therapy (PE), Art Therapy, Writing, Stress Inoculation Therapy, Yoga, and Mindfulness. Other more recent therapies are being developed.

STRESS, FATIGUE, AND SHIFT WORK IN POLICING

The identification of factors associated with shift work adaptation will enable development of interventions that can improve mental health and well-being, as well as prevent accidents, injuries, and diseases linked with shift work and atypical hours (Vena et al., 2014). Waterhouse (2003) suggested that officers may reached an exhaustion phase of the stress response due to maladaptation and the breakdown of endogenous compensatory mechanisms. Maladapted officers had more stress, fatigue and sleep disruption relative to adapted officers, who tended to have better diets, more agreeableness and hardiness, less neuroticism, and more familial support. Biomarkers indicated biological dysregulation in these officers. Work organization and attitudes, coping strategies, and other psychological, social, behavioral and lifestyle factors were also affected.

Factors related to sleep and sleep/wake timing are prominent indicators of shift work adaptation (Burch et al., 2009). The hormone melatonin is a major driver of circadian timekeeping (Kayumov, Zhdanova, & Shapiro, 2000). Officers with disrupted circadian melatonin production may have a higher prevalence of sleepiness, fatigue and mental symptoms relative to those with normal melatonin patterns. Working overtime and secondary employment additionally affect the well-being of officers. Overtime is a necessary, often mandatory part of police work in many jurisdictions due to shortages of personnel. Off-duty court overtime is also a source of fatigue (Vila, 2002). Many police officers also work second jobs, adding the total number of work hours in a day (Vila, 2002). The disconnect in preferred sleep time and timing imposed by social/work obligations is known as "social jet lag" and can lead to sleep debt and development of chronic health conditions (Roenneberg et al., 2012; Shuster, O'Berlinner & Claus, 2019). Social jet lag is not simply the propensity to sleep at a particular time during a 24-hour period but its consequences in the life course of people (Witmann, Dinich, Merrow & Roenneberg, 2006). Social jet lag affects individual variations of sleep/wake times (Wittmann, Dinich, Merrow, & Roenneberg, 2006). Due to shift work and other work schedules, many police officers have dysregulated sleep/wake patterns (Lack, Bailey, Lovato, & Wright, 2009). Cues that are important for either facilitating or disrupting sleep/wake cycles include: light exposure, diet, social behavior, work schedules, body temperature, and the sleeping environment.

Sleep Problems

Shift workers who had difficulties falling asleep or tended to wake up early were less likely to report optimal performance and were less content with their work schedule, whereas optimal performance was associated with the use of sleep aids and an acknowledged need for more sleep (Rajaratnam & Arendt, 2001). Social schedules such as shift work interfere considerably with individual sleep preferences in the majority of the population (Shuster, Oberlinner & Claus, 2019; Lack, Bailey, Livato & Wright, 2009). As an occupational group, police officers often suffer from poor sleep quality and fatigue (Vila, 2002). Night shift work was found to be significantly and independently associated with snoring and decreased sleep duration among police officers (Charles et al., 2007). In a screening of a group of North American police officers, 40% had at least one sleep disorder, including 34.6% with obstructive sleep apnea, 6.5% with moderate to severe insomnia, and 5.4% for shift work disorder. On a sleepiness scale, 28.5% reported excessive sleepiness and 26.1% reported sleepiness while driving at least monthly.

Police officers who screened positive for a sleep disorder more frequently reported making a serious administrative error, falling asleep while driving, making an error or safety violation due to fatigue, showing uncontrolled anger toward suspects, absenteeism, and falling asleep during meetings, as compared to police officers who screened negative for a sleep disorder (Barger et al., 2011). Italian state police officers were studied for sleep patterns, sleep disorders, sleepiness at work, and hypnotic drug intake. Shift workers more often had difficulty in initiating sleep with longer sleep latency and early awakenings were more common. Shift workers frequently reported requiring more sleep (Garbarino, Nobili et al., 2002).The effect of consecutive night shift work on the sleepiness, vigilance, and driving performance of police officers was studied (Waggoner et al., 2012). Sleepiness scores were lower among shift workers as compared to non-shift workers. However, sleep-related accidents were increased among shift workers and related to the presence of indicators of sleep disorders (Garbarino et al., 2001).

Unhealthy Diet Among Shift Workers

Studies indicate higher fat and carbohydrate intake among night shift workers (Roskoden et al., 2017). Lower fruit and vegetable intake also has been observed among shift workers (Hemio et al., 2015; Mota et al., 2014). Timing of eating may also play a key role in determining the health of shift workers. Food consumption acts as an environmental entrainment cue for the body's rhythms and can influence biological clocks. Sleep-deprived individuals may be more likely to make poor dietary choices, as sleep influences appetite-related functions in the brain (Hanlon & Van Cauter, 2011; Greer, Goldstein & Walker, 2013). Short sleep duration is associated with decreased levels of the hormone leptin, which regulates appetite suppression, and elevated levels of the hormone ghrelin, which stimulates hunger (Klok, Jakobsdottir & Drent, 2007).

Sleep quality may play an important role in dietary decision making in shift workers. In a cross-sectional study of urban police officers in the United States, Velazquez-Kronen et al. (2017) classified officers according to four dietary patterns: fruits and vegetables, dairy products, starches and fried foods, and meat and eggs. Officers reporting borderline or poor sleep quality had lower healthy dietary pattern fruits and vegetable intake than those reporting optimal sleep quality, suggesting that better sleep quality is positively associated with greater intake of healthy foods, such as dark green and red-orange vegetables, citrus and other fruits, and beans.

Aging and Shift Work

It is important to understand how aging affects police officers' ability to tolerate shift work since changes in the workforce are resulting in an increasing number of shift workers over age 45. In a study of police officers in three age groups (20–32.9, 33–39.9, and 40 and above), better attitudes towards their shift work, better adjustment to night-bound shifts, greater job satisfaction and organizational commitment, lower fatigue and longer sleep durations were found among younger officers. Alternatively, adaptation among older workers may reflect more job satisfaction, more seniority, greater decision latitude, or a possible survivor effect (Burch et al., 2009).

Injury

Violanti et al. (2013) surveyed work payroll records to study the association of shift work and injury occurrence. Injury was significantly elevated in officers working night (by 72%) and afternoon shifts (by 66%). On the first day back to work, injury occurrence was elevated on the midnight shift compared with working the day shift (by 69%) or afternoon shift (by 54%). The joint combination of working the night shift and having a heavy workload was associated with a 2.3-fold greater occurrence of injury compared with officers working the day shift and having a light workload (Riedy et al., 2020).

Shift Work Interventions

Approaches for managing fatigue in policing should be considered while still providing police departments with the operational flexibility. Unfortunately, many police departments are also chronically understaffed and need scheduling flexibility to meet demands for service. The purpose of fatigue risk management systems is to mitigate fatigue proactively. Examples of such procedures include identifying fatigue hazards, use of predictive fatigue modeling in work scheduling, implementation of proactive fatigue monitoring, and development of education and training programs (Satterfield & Van Dongen, 2013).

Education

Shift work is a challenge that cannot be eliminated and must instead be dealt with through individual and organizational responses to lessen its effect on workers. Officers can work to practice healthy sleep habits, eliminating noise and light from their sleeping area, avoiding caffeine close to bedtime, and avoiding alcohol (National Sleep Foundation, 2011). To help ensure adequate family and social interaction, family and social gatherings could be scheduled to best accommodate the work-sleep schedule. With the physiological challenges associated with traditional night or rotating shifts and also with extended shifts and nonstandard hours, comprehensive fatigue management programs may be of benefit to police officers and organizations. These programs may include education, screening for sleep disorders, and interventions to lessen negative consequences associated with shift work (Barger, Lockley, Rajaratnam, & Landrigan, 2009).

Type of Shift

The type of shift could also be considered in fatigue mitigation including fixed (permanent) shifts; rotating shifts, forward-rotating (day to afternoon then to night) and backward-rotating shifts (night to afternoon then to day); as well as the speed of rotation (slow or fast). These different types of rotation may be associated with different health effects. For example, Demerouti, Geurts, Bakker, and Euwema (2004) examined the impact of rotation and timing of shifts on police to identify methods to lessen the negative consequences of shift work. Shift rotation was related to unfavorable job attitudes and timing was related to increased work-home conflict. Avoiding fixed non-day shifts including weekends was suggested to reduce conflict between work and home and a high degree of flexibility in rotation rosters. Police departments may also choose to change from rotating to permanent shift assignments. This change was made in the Lexington, Kentucky Police Department in 1989. Following the change, sleep quality and sleep hygiene improved. Psychological well-being improved and absenteeism dropped from 1,400 hours in the six months prior to the change to 883 hours during the 6 months following the change (Phillips, Magan, Gerhardstein, & Cecil, 1991).

Martin-Gill et al. (2019) developed performance measures for shift workers based on evidence-based guidelines for fatigue risk management in emergency medical technicians (EMTs). The authors used fatigue and/or sleepiness survey instruments, optimal duration of shifts, access to caffeine as a fatigue countermeasure, use of napping during shift work, and the delivery of education and training on fatigue risk. Five recommendations were submitted:

- Use fatigue/sleepiness survey instruments to measure and monitor fatigue
- Personnel work shifts in shorter duration
- Workers have access to caffeine as a fatigue countermeasure
- Personnel have the opportunity to nap while on duty to mitigate fatigue
- Workers receive education and training to mitigate fatigue and fatigue-related risks

Napping at Work

Napping during work has been suggested as a way to help reduce fatigue during night shifts. There is, however, controversy concerning napping on police duty. Patterson et al. (2020) outlined some of the arguments for and against napping while on duty:

Arguments for On-Duty Napping

- Inadequate sleep, poor sleep, and work-related fatigue.
- Feeling mentally and/or physically fatigued while at work.
- Excessive daytime sleepiness
- Unsatisfactory recovery between scheduled shifts
- Extended shifts, excessive overtime hours, second job
- Excess work intensifies the poor sleep and fatigue problem.

Arguments Against On-Duty Napp[ing

- Likely the most intense argument against napping is a negative public perception of police officers being paid to sleep while on duty. Many citizens and police administrators do not condone napping on duty. Officers are expected to be available at any time to respond to calls and/or emergency situations, and napping on-duty may impair their ability to respond.
- A second argument against napping concerns sleep inertia. Sleep inertia refers to the feeling of disorientation and grogginess upon waking and is usually most severe in the first few minutes after waking. However, some studies have detected its impact on motor function and decision making.

Police organizational efforts may help to reduce impact on morbidity, mortality, injury, and disability among police officers. Additional investment in police officer health and safety related to shift work will provide a direct benefit for officers and law enforcement organizations. However, in the end the individual can best avoid the negative aspects of shift work by getting adequate sleep and practicing good sleep hygiene.

THE BUFFALO CARDIO-METABOLIC OCCUPATIONAL POLICE STRESS (BCOPS) STUDY

As a final precedent, I would like to share some of the findings from the BCOPS study. The BCOPS study is a 16-year longitudinal study on police stress and health led by author of this book. This project benefitted extensively from the experience of the highly skilled interdisciplinary investigative team (including epidemiologists and biostatisticians, psychologists, sociologists, and medical professionals) working together (Violanti, 2020). This study provided new knowledge that is likely to improve a broader understanding of how workplace stressors lead to early adverse cardio metabolic and psychological changes in police officers. Given the high prevalence of cardiovascular disease among police officers, any decrease in occupationally related risk factors could have a significant public health impact and stimulate future intervention studies documenting evidence-based recommendations on how to best improve the health consequences of workplace stress.

There were four areas of investigation in the BCOPS study where significant changes occurred over time: (1) lifestyle, (2) work related and psychological conditions, (3) cardiovascular measures including metabolic syndrome components, and (4) imbalance in stress hormones. Examples of physiological measures included blood pressure, autonomic nervous functioning, height, weight, body mass index (BMI), percent body fat, abdominal obesity, waist circumference and bone density. The study assessed carotid artery thickness (plaque buildup) and artery expansion health with ultrasound. Small vessels in the eye were examined for damage as an indicator of future cardiovascular health. Hormones known to be biological markers of stress (e.g. cortisol) were measured using saliva samples. Psychological measures included post-traumatic stress disorder (PTSD), depression, anxiety, suicide ideation, and others. Measures considered protective against stress were resiliency and social support. Information on sleep quantity and quality were obtained from body-worn monitoring devices that provided continuous recording of movement data without the need for technical assistance or overnight stays in the laboratory.

The results thus far indicate that police health and well-being are not improving at a desirable pace and that more research and care is needed for police officers. Some preliminary BCOPS study results so far:

- Overall the longitudinal measure of police work stressors increased significantly over the study period. Scores remained high.
- Overall, indicators of poorer cardiovascular health worsened among police. A decrease in brachial artery reactivity (artery health indicator) and an increased thickness in the carotid artery occurred over time.
- Cortisol is a stress hormone, and changes in normal cortisol patterns influence pathological physiological outcomes. Abnormal cortisol patterns predicted worsening of artery health in male officers over time.
- Higher stress ratings were related to abnormal cortisol patterns, suggesting that police stressors may result in biological dysfunctions related to stress. Abused children, shootings, and assaults affected stress levels the most. This will allow interventional focusing on these specific high level stressors.
- Findings indicating that low organizational support increased stress suggested that policy should be changed to increase support mechanisms at work, including increased participation in decision making and leadership training.
- Sustained higher exposure to occupational stressors over time was significantly and independently associated with elevated levels of depression symptoms in police officers. Individuals with depression are more likely to develop coronary artery disease.
- The level of post-traumatic stress disorder (PTSD) symptoms remained higher than expected over time. Depression was related with PTSD and psychological dissociation among officers.

Both PTSD and depression may promote poor health through a complex interaction between biological and psychological mechanisms.

- Findings on depression indicated that sustained higher exposure to occupational stressors over the study period was significantly and independently associated with elevated levels of depressive symptoms in police officers.
- Resiliency (considered protective against stress) decreased over time.
- Officers who were fatigued had a significantly higher prevalence of workplace injury. Poor sleep quality and fatigue were associated with injuries.
- The odds of absenteeism increased as on-duty fatigue and sleepiness increased and prior sleep decreased. This was particularly evident for swing shift officers and night shift officers who were predicted to obtain less sleep and have greater fatigue and sleepiness than day shift officers.
- Long-term associations were found between sleep quality and increased risk of poor artery health. Based on results concerning sleep deprivation and shift work, recommendations were made to police agencies to add sleep hygiene practices to their training regimens. Together with this finding was an association with a significant increase in the number of regular and overtime hours per week.
- Heart rate variability (HRV) is an indicator of a healthy heart rhythm. This study found that that good physical condition may help to increase the heart rate variability among officers. Higher levels of physical activity, lower levels of obesity predicted higher levels of HRV.

Presentation of BCOPS findings were made before two presidential commissions on law enforcement (President's Commission on 21st Century Policing, 2015 and President's Commission on Law Enforcement, 2020) laying the groundwork for police agencies to utilize information gained from these commissions for mental and physical health of officers. Additionally, recent national legislation has implemented a mental health program for police. The Community Oriented Police Services (COPS–U.S. Department of Justice) has held several conferences using this study and it has been widely distributed.

Police agencies can use the results from this study to inform policy decisions and educate police officers on factors of lifestyle and wellness. For example, results from shift work analyses show that the quality and quantity of sleep that officers get is deficient leading to higher rates of fatigue and injury across time. Training in sleep hygiene and possible policies that adjust shift work schedules or initiate possible interventions like controlled napping and caffeine intake may help. Decreasing cardiovascular health can be reduced by establishing wellness programs that emphasize exercise, diet, sleep, and stress management.

There have been many police wellness programs that utilized BCOPS findings. We do not yet have the documentation or ability to evaluate police wellness programs which utilized our findings in their programs and training and how stress and disease have been decreased. We do know that legislation has moved police policy in the direction of improving officer's mental and physical health. The president's bill on police mental health and suicide prevention (2020) is one example. We will continue to analyze data and disseminate information long after the completion of this study in order to provide additional findings which are important to police and academic research.

REFERENCES

Andrew, M. E., Violanti, J. M., Gu, J. K., Fekedulegn, D., Li, S., Hartley, T. A., . . . Burchfiel, C. M. (2017). Police work stressors and cardiac vagal control. *American Journal of Human Biology, 29*(5), 1–17.

Arias, A. J., Steinberg, K., Banga, A., & Trestman, R. L. (2006). Systematic review of the efficacy of meditation techniques as treatments for medical illness. *Journal of Alternative and Complementary Medicine, 12,* 817–832.

Baer, R. A., Lykins, Emily L.B., & Peters, Jessica R. (2012). Mindfulness and self-compassion as predictors of psychological wellbeing in long-term meditators and matched nonmeditators. *The Journal of Positive Psychology, 7*(3), 230-238. doi: 10.1080/17439760.2012.674548

Barger, L. K., Lockley, S. W., Rajaratnam, S. M., & Landrigan, C. P. (2009). Neurobehavioral, health, and safety consequences associated with shift work in safety-sensitive professions. *Current Neurology and Neuroscience Reports, 9*(2), 155–164. https://doi.org/10.1007/s11910-009-0024-7

Barker, R. T., & Camarata, M. R. (1998). The role of communication in creating and maintaining a learning organization: Preconditions, indicators, and disciplines. *The Journal of Business Communication, 35*(4), 443-467. doi:10.1177/002194369803 500402

Beetz, A., Uvnas-Moberg, K., Julius, H., & Kotrschal, K. (2012). Psychosocial and psychophysiological effects of human-animal interactions: The possible role of oxytocin. *Frontiers in Psychology, 3,* 234. https://doi.org/10.3389/fpsyg.2012 .00234

Berger, W., Coutinho, E. S., Figueira, I., Marques-Portella, C., Luz, M. P., Neylan, T. C., . . . Mendlowicz, M. V. (2012). Rescuers at risk: A systematic review and meta-regression analysis of the worldwide current prevalence and correlates of PTSD in rescue workers. *Social Psychiatry and Psychiatric Epidemiology, 47*(6), 1001–1011. https://doi.org/10.1007/s00127-011-0408-2

Bergman, A. L., Christopher, M. S., & Bowen, S. (2016). Changes in facets of mindfulness predict stress and anger outcomes for police officers. *Mindfulness, 7*(4), 851–858. https://doi.org/10.1007/s12671-016-0522-z

Bishop, S. R., Lau, M., Shapiro, S., Carlson, L., Anderson, N. D., Carmody, J., . . . Devins, G. (2004). Mindfulness: A proposed operational definition. *Clinical Psychology: Science and Practice, 11*(3), 230–241. https://doi.org/10.1093/clipsy .bph077

Burch, J. B., Tom, J., Zhai, Y., Criswell, L., Leo, E., & Ogoussan, K. (2009). Shiftwork impacts and adaptation among health care workers. *Occupational Medicine, 59,* 159-166.

Burke, R. J. (2017). Stress in policing: An overview. In R. J. Burke (Ed.), *Stress in policing: Sources, consequences, and interventions* (pp. 3–28). London: Routledge.

Bussing, A., Michalsen, A., Khalsa, S. B., Telles, S., & Sherman, K. J. (2012). Effects of yoga on mental and physical health: A short summary of reviews. *Evidence-Based Complementary and Alternative Medicine, 2012,* 165-410.

Castellano, C. (2012). Reciprocal Peer Support (RPS): A decade of not so random acts of kindness. *International Journal of Emergency Mental Health, 14*(2), 105–110.

Chinman, M., George, P., Dougherty, R. H., Daniels, A. S., Ghose, S. S., Swift, A., & Delphin-Rittmon, M. E. (2014). Peer support services for individuals with serious mental illnesses: Assessing the evidence. *Psychiatric Services (Washington, D.C.), 65*(4), 429–441. https://doi.org/10.1176/appi.ps.201300244

Chopko, B. A., & Schwartz, R. C. (2013). The relation between mindfulness and posttraumatic stress symptoms among police officers. *Journal of Loss and Trauma, 18*(1), 1–9. https://doi.org/10.1080/15325024.2012.674442

Cloitre, M. (2015). The "one size fits all" approach to trauma treatment: Should we be satisfied? *European Journal of Psychotraumatology, 6,* 27344. https://doi.org/10 .3402/ejpt.v6.27344

Cloitre, M., Garvert, D. W., Brewin, C. R., Bryant, R. A., & Maercker, A. (2013). Evidence for proposed ICD-11 PTSD and complex PTSD: A latent profile analysis. *European Journal of Psychotraumatology, 4,* 10.3402/ejpt.v4i0.20706. https://doi.org/10.3402/ejpt.v4i0.20706

Cloitre, M. (2009). Effective psychotherapies for posttraumatic stress disorder: A review and critique. *CNS Spectrum, 14*(1 Suppl 1), 32-43.

Chumley, P. R. (2012). Historical perspectives of the human-animal bond within the Department of Defense. *U.S. Army Medical Department Journal*, 18–20.

Collins, S. M., Karasek, R. A., & Costas, K. (2005). Job strain and autonomic indices of cardiovascular disease risk. *American Journal of Industrial Medicine, 48,* 182–193.

Cooper, C. L., Davidson, M. J., & Robinson, P. (1982). Stress in the police service. *Journal of Occupational Medicine, 24*(1), 30–36.

Crank, J. P., & Caldero, M. (1991). The production of occupational stress in medium-sized police agencies: A survey of line officers in eight municipal departments. *Journal of Criminal Justice, 19*(4), 339–349.

Davidson, L., Bellamy, C., Guy, K., & Miller, R. (2012). Peer support among persons with severe mental illnesses: A review of evidence and experience. *World Psychiatry: Official Journal of the World Psychiatric Association (WPA), 11*(2), 123–128. https://doi.org/10.1016/j.wpsyc.2012.05.009

Demerouti, E., Geurts, S. A., Bakker, A. B., & Euwema, M. (2004). The impact of shiftwork on work–home conflict, job attitudes and health. *Ergonomics, 47*(9), 987–1002. https://doi.org/10.1080/00140130410001670408

Digliani, J. A. (2015). Peer support. *Contemporary Issues in Police Psychology*, Chapter 2, p. 3.

Digliani, J. A. (2019). The PAC program. Annual Mental Health Check.

Everly, G., Smith, K.J. & Lobo, R. (2013). Resilient leadership and the organizational culture of resilience: Construct validation. *International Journal of Emergency Mental Health, 15*(2), 123–128.

Feigelman, W., Feigelman, B., & Range, L. M. (2020). Grief and healing trajectories of drug-death-bereaved parents. *OMEGA–Journal of Death and Dying, 80*(4), 629–647. https://doi.org/10.1177/0030222818754669

Finney, C., Stergiopoulos, E., Hensel, J., Bonato, S., & Dewa, C. S. (2013). Organizational stressors associated with job stress and burnout in correctional officers: A systematic review. *British Medical Journal Public Health, 13*(82), 1–13.

Garbarino, S., De Carli, F., Mascialino, B., Beelke, M., Nobili, L., Squarcia, S., . . . Ferrillo, F. (2001). Sleepiness in a population of Italian shiftwork policemen. *Journal of Human Ergonomics (Tokyo), 30*(1–2), 211–216.

Goyal, M., Singh, S., Sibinga, E. M., Gould, N. F., Rowland-Seymour, A., Sharma, R., . . . Haythornthwaite, J. A. (2014). Meditation programs for psychological stress and well-being: A systematic review and meta-analysis. *JAMA Internal Medicine, 174*(3), 357–368. https://doi.org/10.1001/jamainternmed.2013.13018.

Greer, S. M., Goldstein, A. N., & Walker, M. P. (2013). The impact of sleep deprivation on food desire in the human brain. *Nature Communications, 4,* 2259. doi:10.1038/ncomms3259

Hampl, J. S., Anderson, J. V., Mullis, R., & American Dietetic Association. (2002). Position of the American Dietetic Association: The role of dietetics professionals in health promotion and disease prevention. *Journal of the American Dietetic Association, 102*(11), 1680–1687. https://doi.org/10.1016/s0002-8223(02)90359-7

Hanlon, E. C., & Van Cauter, E. (2011). Quantification of sleep behavior and of its impact on the cross-talk between the brain and peripheral metabolism. *Proceedings of the National Academy of Sciences of the United States of America, 108 Suppl 3*, 15609–15616, doi:10.1073/pnas.1101338108.

Hartley, T. A., Shankar, A., Fekedulegn, D., Violanti, J. M., Andrew, M. E., Knox, S. S., & Burchfiel, C. M. (2011). Metabolic syndrome and carotid intima media thickness in urban police officers. *Journal of Occupational and Environmental Medicine, 53*(5), 553–561.

Heart Disease. CDC, https://www.cdc.gov/heartdisease/index.htm. Accessed 3-16-2021

Hemio, K., Puttonen, S., Viitasalo, K., H‰rm‰, M., Peltonen, M., & Lindstrˆm, J. (2015). Food and nutrient intake among workers with different shift systems. *Occupational and Environmental Medicine, 72*(7), 513–520. https://doi.org/10.1136/oemed-2014-102624

Johnson, D. C., Thom, N. J., Stanley, E. A., Haase, L., Simmons, A. N., Shih, P. A., . . . Paulus, M. P. (2014). Modifying resilience mechanisms in at-risk individuals: A controlled study of mindfulness training in Marines preparing for deployment. *The American Journal of Psychiatry, 171*(8), 844–853. https://doi.org/10.1176/appi.ajp.2014.13040502

Joseph, N. P., Violanti, J. M., Donahue, R., Andrew, M. E., Trevisan, M., Burchfiel, C. M., & Dorn J. (2009). Police work and subclinical atherosclerosis. *Journal of Occupational and Environmental Medicine, 51*(6), 700–707.

Kabat-Zinn, J. (1990). *Full catastrophe living: Using the wisdom of your body and mind to face stress, pain, and illness.* New York: Dell Publishing, pp. 1–20.

Kabat-Zinn, J. (2003). Mindfulness-based interventions in context: Past, present, and future. *Clinical Psychology: Science and Practice, 10*(2), 144–156. https://doi.org/10.1093/clipsy.bpg016

Keng, S. L., Smoski, M. J., & Robins, C. J. (2011). Effects of mindfulness on psychological health: A review of empirical studies. *Clinical Psychology Review, 31*(6), 1041–1056. https://doi.org/10.1016/j.cpr.2011.04.006

Kelley, T., & Lambert, E. (2012). Mindfulness as a potential means of attenuating anger and aggression for prospective criminal justice professionals. *Mindfulness, 3*(4), 261–274.

Klatt, M. D., Buckworth, J., & Malarkey, W. B. (2009). Effects of low-dose mindfulness-based stress reduction (MBSR-ld) on working adults. *Health Education & Behavior: The Official Publication of the Society for Public Health Education, 36*(3), 601–614. https://doi.org/10.1177/1090198108317627

Klok, M. D., Jakobsdottir, S., & Drent, M. L. (2007). The role of leptin and ghrelin in the regulation of food intake and body weight in humans: A review. *Obesity Reviews: An Official Journal of the International Association for the Study of Obesity, 8*, 21–34. doi:10.1111/j.1467-789X.2006.00270.x.

Kuehl, K. S., Elliot, D. L., MacKinnon, D. P., O'Rourke, H. P., DeFrancesco, C., Miocevic, M., . . . Kuehl, H. (2016). The SHIELD (safety & health improvement: Enhancing law enforcement departments) study: Mixed methods longitudinal findings. *Journal of Occupational and Environmental Medicine, 58*(5), 492–498. https://doi.org/10.1097/JOM.0000000000000716

Lack, L., Bailey, M., Lovato, N., & Wright, H. (2009). Chronotype differences in circadian rhythms of temperature, melatonin, and sleepiness as measured in a modified constant routine protocol. *Nature and Science of Sleep, 1,* 1–8. PMC 3630920. PMID 23616692. Bottom of Form

Landers, G. M., & Zhou, M. (2011). An analysis of relationships among peer support, psychiatric hospitalization, and crisis stabilization. *Community Mental Health Journal, 47*(1), 106–112. https://doi.org/10.1007/s10597-009-9218-3

Leiter, M. P., & Maslach, C. (2004). Areas of work life: A structured approach to organizational predictors of job burnout. In P. Perrewé & D. C. Ganster (Eds.), *Research in occupational stress and well-being* (pp. 91–134). Oxford, United Kingdom: Elsevier.

Leiter, M. P. (1992). Burnout as a crisis in professional role structures: Measurement and conceptual issues. *Anxiety, Stress, & Coping, 5,* 79–93.

Law Enforcement Suicide Data Collection Act (134 STAT. 644 PUBLIC LAW 116–143–JUNE 16, 2020 Public Law 116–143 116th Congress, June 16, 2020). Approved June 16, 2020.

Libby, D. J., Reddy, F., Pilver, C. E., & Desai, R. A. (2012). The use of yoga in specialized VA PTSD treatment programs. *International Journal of Yoga Therapy, 22*(1), 79–87.

Martin-Gill, C., Barger, L. K., Moore, C. G., Higgins, J. S., Teasley, E. M., Weiss, P. M. . . . Patterson, P. D. (2018). Effects of napping during shift work on sleepiness and performance in emergency medical services personnel and similar shift workers: A systematic review and meta-analysis. *Prehospital Emergency Care: Official Journal of the National Association of EMS Physicians and the National Association of State EMS Directors, 22*(suppl. 1), 47–57. https://doi.org/10.1080/10903127.2017.1376136

Mead, S., Hilton, D., & Curtis, L. (2001). Peer support: A theoretical perspective. *Psychiatric Rehabilitation Journal, 25*(2), 134–141. https://doi.org/10.1037/h0095032

Mota, M. C., Silva, C. M., Balieiro, L., GonÁalves, B. F., Fahmy, W. M., & Crispim, C. A. (2019). Association between social jetlag food consumption and meal times in patients with obesity-related chronic diseases. *PloS one, 14*(2), e0212126. https://doi.org/10.1371/journal.pone.0212126

Nachreiner, F. (1998). Individual and social determinants of shiftwork tolerance. *Scand J Work Environ Health, 24,* 35–42.

National Institute of Justice. Safety, Health, and Wellness Strategic Research Plan. (2016-2021). U.S. Department of Justice, Office of Justice Programs 810 Seventh St. N.W. Washington, DC 20531, http://www.NIJ.gov

National Sleep Foundation. Sleep Disorder. https://www.sleepfoundation.org/

O'Malley & Nice (2016). *Operation Thrive Wellness Challenge.* Accessed 9-19-20. https://www.fbinaa.org/FBINAA/Staying on theYBR.aspx.

Parenti, L., Wilson, M., Foreman, A. M., Wirth, O., & Meade, B. J. (2015). Selecting quality service dogs: Part 1: Morphological and health considerations. *The APDT Chronicle of the Dog,* (summer), 71–77.

Patterson, P. D., Weaver, M. D., Guyette, F. X., & Martin-Gill, C. (2020). Should public safety shift workers be allowed to nap while on duty? *American Journal of Industrial Medicine, 63*(10), 843–850. Advance online publication. https://doi.org/10.1002/ajim.23164

Paton, D. (2000). Emergency planning: Integrating community development, community resilience and hazard mitigation. *J Am Soc Prof Emerg Manag, 7,* 109–118.

Paton, D., Smith, L., Violanti, J. M., & Er‰onen, L. (2000). Work-related traumatic stress: Risk, vulnerability and resilience. In J. M. Violanti, D. Paton, & C. Dunning (Eds.), *Posttraumatic stress intervention: Challenges, issues, and perspectives* (pp. 187–204). Springfield, IL: Charles C Thomas, Publisher, Ltd.

Phillips, B., Magan, L., Gerhardstein, C., & Cecil, B. (1991). Shift work, sleep quality, and worker health: A study of police officers. *Southern Medical Journal, 84*(10), 1176–1196. https://doi.org/10.1097/00007611-199110000-00005

Police Executive Research Forum. Officer Safety and Wellness (2018). https://cops.usdoj.gov/officersafetyandwellness. Accessed 3-16-21.

Purba, A., & Demou, E. (2019). The relationship between organizational stressors and mental well-being within police officers: A systematic review. *BMC Public Health, 19*(1286), 1–21.

Ramey, S. L., Downing, N. R., Franke, W. D., Perkhounkova, Y., & Alasagheirin, M. H. (2012). Relationships among stress measures, risk factors, and inflammatory biomarkers in law enforcement officers. *Biological Research for Nursing, 14*(1), 16–26. https://doi.org/10.1177/1099800410396356

Riedy, S. M., Roach, G. D., & Dawson, D. (2020). Sleep-wake behaviors exhibited by shift workers in normal operations and predicted by a biomathematical model of fatigue. *Sleep, 43*(9), zsaa049. https://doi.org/10.1093/sleep/zsaa049

Roenneberg, T., Allebrandt, K. V., Merrow, M., & Vetter, C. (2012). Social jetlag and obesity. *Current Biology, 22,* 939–943.

Roskoden, F. C., Kroger, J., Vogt, L. J., Gortner, S., Hannich, H. J., Steveling, A., Lerch, M. M., & Aghdassi, A. A. (2017). Physical activity, energy expenditure, nutritional habits, quality of sleep and stress levels in shift-working health care personnel. *PloS One, 12*(1), e0169983. https://doi.org/10.1371/journal.pone.0169983

Salzer, M. S., & Shear, S. L. (2002). Identifying consumer-provider benefits in evaluations of consumer-delivered services. *Psychiatric Rehabilitation Journal, 25*(3), 281–288. https://doi.org/10.1037/h0095014

Satterfield, B. C., & Van Dongen, H. P. A. (2013). Occupational fatigue, underlying sleep and circadian mechanisms, and approaches to fatigue risk management. *Fatigue 1,* 118–136.

Schuster, M., Oberlinner, C., & Claus, M. (2019). Shift-specific associations between age, chronotype and sleep duration. *Chronobiology International, 36*(6), 784–795. doi: 10.1080/07420528.2019.1586719. Epub 2019

Shane, J. M. (2010). Organizational stressors and police performance. *Journal of Criminal Justice, 38*(4), 807–818. https://doi.org/10.1016/j.jcrimjus.2010.05.008

Shapiro, F., & Forrest, M. S. (1997). *EMDR: The breakthrough therapy for overcoming anxiety, stress, and trauma.* New York, NY: Basic Books, pp. 10–20.

Shapiro, F., & Maxfield, L. (2002). Eye movement desensitization and reprocessing (EMDR): Information processing in the treatment of trauma. *Journal of Clinical Psychology, 58*(8), 933–946. https://doi.org/10.1002/jclp.10068

Sharpless, B. A., & Barber, J. P. (2011). A clinician's guide to PTSD treatments for returning veterans. *Professional Psychology: Research and Practice, 42*(1), 8–15. https://doi.org/10.1037/a0022351

Siegrist, M., & Cvetkovich, G. (2000). Perception of hazards: The role of social trust and knowledge. *Risk Analysis, 20*(5), 713–719. https://doi.org/10.1111/0272-4332.205064

Silver, S. M., Rogers, S., & Russell, M. (2008). Eye movement desensitization and reprocessing (EMDR) in the treatment of war veterans. *Journal of Clinical Psychology, 64*(8), 947–957. https://doi.org/10.1002/jclp.20510

Solomon, P. (2004). Peer support/peer provided services underlying processes, benefits, and critical ingredients. *Psychiatric Rehabilitation Journal, 27*(4), 392–401. https://doi.org/10.2975/27.2004.392.401

Souter, M. A., & Miller, M. D. (2007). Do animal-assisted activities effectively treat depression: A meta-analysis. In *Database of Abstracts of Reviews of Effects (DARE): Quality-assessed Reviews [Internet].* York (UK): Centre for Reviews and Dissemination (UK); 1995-. Available from: https://www.ncbi.nlm.nih.gov/books/NBK74080/

Spence, D. L., Fox, M., Moore, G. C., Estill, S., & Comrie, N. E. A. (2019). *Law Enforcement Mental Health and Wellness Act: Report to Congress.* Washington, DC: U.S. Department of Justice.

Tanigoshi, H., Kontos, A. P., & Remley, Jr., T. P. (2008). The effectiveness of individual wellness counseling on the wellness of law enforcement officers. *Journal of Counseling & Development, 86*(1), 64–86.

Telles, S., Singh, N., & Balkrishna, A. (2012). Managing mental health disorders resulting from trauma through yoga: A review. *Depression Research and Treatment, 2012,* 401–513.

Thompson, P. D., Franklin, B. A., Balady, G. J., Blair, S. N., Corrado, D., Estes, N. A. . . . American College of Sports Medicine. (2007). Exercise and acute cardiovascular events placing the risks into perspective: A scientific statement from the American Heart Association Council on Nutrition, Physical Activity, and Metabolism and the Council on Clinical Cardiology. *Circulation, 115*(17), 2358–2368. https://doi.org/10.1161/CIRCULATIONAHA.107.181485

Tyagi, A., & Dhar, R. L. (2014). Factors affecting health of the police official: Mediating role of job stress. *Policing: An International Journal of Police Strategies & Management, 37*(3), 649–664.

Varvarigou, V., Farioli, A., Korre, M., Sato, S., Dahabreh, I. J., & Kales, S. N. (2014). Law enforcement duties and sudden cardiac death among police officers in United States: Case distribution study. *BMJ (Clinical research education), 349,* g6534. https://doi.org/10.1136/bmj.g6534

Velazquez-Kronen et al. (2017). *Sleep quality and dietary patterns in an occupational cohort of police officers.* Society for Epidemiological Research Annual Conference, Seattle, June 20–23, 2017.

Vila, B. (2006). Impact of long work hours on police officers and the communities they serve. *American Journal of Industrial Medicine, 49*(11), 972–980. doi: 10.1002/ajim.20333

Vila, B., & Police Executive Research Forum. (2000). *Tired cops: The importance of managing police fatigue.* Washington, D.C.: Police Executive Research Forum.

Violanti, J. M. (2011). Police organizational stress: The impact of negative discipline. *International Journal of Emergency Mental Health, 13*(1), 31–36.

Violanti, J. M., Fekedulegn, D., Andrew, M. E., Charles, L. E., Hartley, T. A., Vila, B., & Burchfiel, C. M. (2013). Shift work and long term injury among police officers. *Scandinavian Journal of Work and Environmental Health, 39*, 361–368.

Violanti, J. M., Andrew, M. E., Mnatsakanova, A., Hartley, T. A., Fekedulegn, D., & Burchfiel, C. M. (2016). Correlates of hopelessness in the high suicide risk police occupation. *Police Practice and Research, 17*(5), 408–419.

Violanti, J. M., Fekedulegn, D., Shi, M., & Andrew, M. E. (2020). Hidden danger: A 22-years analysis of law enforcement deaths associated with duty-related illness (1997–2018). *Policing: An International Journal, 43*(2), 330–344. doi.org/10.1108/PIJPSM-07-2019-0109.

Violanti, J. M. (2020). Final Report. Buffalo Cardio-Metabolic Occupational Police Stress (BCOPS) study. CDC/NIOSH.

Waggoner, L. B., Grant, D. A., Van Dongen, H. P., Belenky, G., & Vila, B. (2012). A combined field and laboratory design for assessing the impact of night shift work on police officer operational performance. *Sleep, 35*(11), 1575–1577. doi: 10.5665/sleep.2214.

Waterhouse, J., Buckley, P., Edwards, B., & Reilly, T. (2003). Measurement of, and some reasons for, differences in eating habits between night and day workers. *Chronobiology International, 20*, 1075–1092.

Wester, S. R., Arndt, D., Sedivy, S. K., & Arndt, L. (2010). Male police officers and stigma associated with counseling: The role of anticipated risks, anticipated benefits and gender role conflict. *Psychology of Men & Masculinity, 11*(4), 286–302. https://doi.org/10.1037/a0019108

Williams, V., Ciarrochi, J., & Deane, F. P. (2010). On being mindful, emotionally aware, and more resilient: Longitudinal pilot study of police recruits. *Australian Psychologist, 45*(4), 274–282. https://doi.org/10.1080/00050060903573197

Wittmann, M., Dinich, J., Merrow, M., & Roenneberg, T. (2006) Social jetlag: Misalignment of biological and social time. *Chronobiology International, 23*, 497–509.

Wupperman, P., Marlatt, G. A., Cunningham, A., Bowen, S., Berking, M., Mulvihill-Rivera, N., & Easton, C. (2012). Mindfulness and modification therapy for behavioral dysregulation: Results from a pilot study targeting alcohol use and aggression in women. *Journal of Clinical Psychology, 68*(1), 50–66. https://doi.org/10.1002/jclp.20830

Zimmerman, F. H. (2012). Cardiovascular disease and risk factors in law enforcement personnel: A comprehensive review. *Cardiology in Review, 20*(4), 159–166. https://doi.org/10.1097/CRD.0b013e318248d631

EPILOGUE

Throughout this volume, the suggestion has been put forth that there is indeed mental and physical health crises among police. Police work is a dangerous profession; however, poor mental and physical health should not be a reason to die from work. One may conclude from this book that the physical and mental health of police officers is adversely affected by exposures in police work and that many factors related to stress, mental health, and disease outcomes have increased over time. Exposure to police work has been shown to lead to an earlier average age at death and a higher prevalence of cardiovascular disease compared to that of the general population. Health disparities increase as officerís age and retire, nearly doubling by the 6th decade and exceeding a two-fold increased risk by the 7th decade.

The interventions suggested in this book are examples of potential strategies to help mitigate stress and adverse health outcomes among police. They are taken from researchers and from police practitioners working in the field. It is suggested that police departments use the material in this book to inform policy decisions and educate police officers on factors of stress, trauma, and lifestyle wellness. Although there appears to be an increase in wellness programs in policing, we do not yet have a firm grasp on the efficacy of the various programs. Future consideration for police health research is the evaluation of programs which best address reduction of disease and mental health outcomes. More exploration is needed for intervention at both organizational and individual levels as we vigorously continue to address the mental and physical health crises in police work. In the end, such work will not only benefit police officers but the public as well.

INDEX

145